THE HABITABLE EARTH

THE HABITABLE
EARTH

by

Ronald Fraser

Line drawings by Jack Worsley

HODDER AND STOUGHTON

Printed in Great Britain for Hodder and Stoughton Limited,
St. Paul's House, Warwick Lane, London, E.C.4,
by Billing & Sons Limited, Guildford and London

For

Allan and Bill

with love and gratitude

Introduction

UNTIL the earthquake-hunters took over, man's knowledge of the structure of his pear-shaped planet was confined to the more superficial regions of the earth's crust. The tools of the classical geology of the nineteenth century – the heyday of the great pioneers like Chambers and Lyell and Geikie – were the geologist's hammer and the bit-borer of the oil-well.

It is therefore hardly surprising that such a limited range of observational techniques, applied moreover exclusively to the outermost skin of the granitic rafts which are the earth's land masses, should have led to quite a few wrong conclusions about the earth as a whole.

Thus today the following nineteenth-century notions have been publicly discarded by all forward-looking geologists: a cooling and shrinking globe; crustal shortening; conventional theories of mountain building:* the ocean basins as submerged land masses, where one might seek the lost Atlantis; or in the case of the Pacific, as a hole left in the earth's crust by the retreating Moon.

The history of the scientific exploration of the interior of the earth is synonymous with the history of the development of the science of *seismology*, the study of earthquakes by the earthquake-hunters, the *seismologists*, who detect and record the earth tremors arising from sporadic cracks and slippage in the solid substance of the earth, literally "from China to Peru" or again "from Greenland's icy mountains to India's coral strand".

The seismologists have set up a world network of *seismographs* –instruments cunningly designed to respond to the passage beneath them of the *seismic waves* which radiate from the focus of each and every earthquake – and they read into the messages received on their *seismograms* a specification of the internal structure of th eglobe.

* In the incantatory language of convention "an orogene preceded by a geosyncline, receiving an immediate influx of bathyal sediments, followed by the accumulation of synorogenic flysch sediments preceding the first folding phase."

7

The story of this major co-operative undertaking begins in 1897 with Richard Oldham of the Geological Society of London, who was the first to distinguish *two kinds* of seismic wave, the so-called P and S waves of Chapter 1. Then came the patient analysis of the enormous mass of data accumulated by the seismographs of a score of different countries, culminating in 1940 with the publication of the *J—B Tables* by Sir Harold Jeffreys of Cambridge, England, and his pupil Kenneth Bullen of Sydney, Australia, of the travel times from source to seismograph of thousands of earthquakes, deep and shallow, large and small. These celebrated Tables, when deciphered with the X-ray eyes of the seismologist, describe in astonishingly fine detail the internal structure of the earth.

Thus the *J–B Tables* of 1940 demonstrated beyond cavil the existence of a *liquid inner core*, surrounded by a massive *semiplastic 'mantle'*, the whole sheathed by the thin *crust* of the continents and ocean floor. Crust, mantle, and inner liquid core: and to these must be added a small *central core*, first spotted by Miss I. Lehmann of Copenhagen in Denmark as early as 1936, in her classical analysis of the P and S waves radiating from two several earthquakes in far-away New Zealand; and ten years later shown by Bullen to be *solid*.

Next, Beno Gutenberg of Pasadena in California, as the result of a detailed examination of a series of comparatively shallow quakes, demonstrated in 1953 the existence of the so-called 'Gutenberg channel' – a narrow zone in the upper mantle in which the substance of the mantle is less rigid and more plastic than is that of the remainder.

In 1952 there occurred a world-shaking earthquake in the mantle beneath Kamchatka in Eastern Siberia, which gave Hugo Benioff, a pupil of Gutenberg, furiously to think – of the earth ringing as one large spherical bell; and which led C. L. Pekeris in Israel to calculate the natural modes of vibration of an earth constructed on the model proposed by Bullen-Gutenberg – solid central core, liquid inner core, solid-mantle-sandwich with a plastic filling near the top, thin crust of basaltic rock under the oceans, granites and schists and gneisses and their detritus below the superficial surface of the land masses.

The prospect of such a verification of his ideas excited Bullen, in the course of his Einstein Memorial Lecture at Adelaide on October 1 1959, to exclaim, with rare scientific detachment:

8

"We should like a few more world-shaking earthquakes to be sure that Benioff's observations are indeed genuine"! Well, his wish was granted in the Chile earthquake of May 22 1960, which as we shall see verified the correctness of the 'B–G model' in every detail.

And finally, in the atomic age, with Bullen as foreman, the seismologists are busy beating yet another lethal sword into a pacific ploughshare. Atomic explosions, particularly if they be below ground, are the ideal seismological tool; because the *time of initiation* of the resulting artificial quake is known to a split second, instead of having to be inferred, as is the case with the vast majority of natural earthquakes.

Thus today the instant of detonation of a test bomb buried below ground in say the Nevada Desert is made public property, in marked contrast to the childish secrecy which for years surrounded the times of explosion of the Bikini bombs in March, April and May 1954 – which anyway were deduced in short order by Bullen with an accuracy of the order of a fifth of a second. So we may perhaps be allowed the hope that the atom bomb will join bows and arrows, pikes, halberds, boiling lead, chain shot, hand grenades and tank traps on the scrap heap of our war museums; but that controlled underground atomic explosions, harmless to man or beast, may lead to a still more detailed knowledge than we have today of the internal structure of our home-in-space – Mother Earth.

For, as we shall learn in this book, mankind should increasingly realise that he is her child, sheltered and sustained by her Mantle – just as are the mountain peaks he so loves to climb, the valleys down whose slopes he runs on skis, the great plains he crosses on safari after lion and antelope; or the seas he navigates in pedallo, dinghy, oil-tanker, or ocean-going liner: and so also (maybe) Sophia, playing in the world and delighting to be with the children of men.

Acknowledgments

Nobody could write a book like this out of his own head. He must know what work is in progress, and the previous knowledge on which it is based. The first is largely a matter of personal contacts with working scientists—and here I have been fortunate. The second is to be found in text-books, monographs, and scientific journals.

Among the sources of written information I have gone to, I should like to acknowledge my particular debt to the following: Beno Gutenberg—*Physics of the Earth's Interior*, Academic Press 1959; Jacobs, Russell and Tuzo Wilson—*Physics and Geology*, McGraw-Hill 1959; Francis P. Shepard—*The Earth Beneath the Sea*, Oxford University Press 1959; W. S. von Arx—*Introduction to Physical Oceanography*, Addison-Wesley Publishing Company 1962; *Continental Drift*, edited by S. K. Runcorn, Academic Press 1962; and to the invaluable résumés of *Scientific American*.

Contents

Introduction

The Plates

15

The subjects illustrated in the plates come from the following sources:

1. Mount Wilson and Palomar Observatiories
2. Fox Photos Ltd.
3. Indian Tourist Information Bureau
4. Camera Press Ltd.
5. A. S. Laughton
6. Dr. A. P. Willmore and Hilger and Watts Ltd.
7. U.K. Atomic Energy Authority
8. U.S. National Science Foundation, and Global Marine Exploration Company
9. Geological Survey of Canada
10. Widerøe's Flyvelskap, Oslo
11. *Challenger Report*, Vol. I, Part 1
12. Woods Hole Oceanographic Institution
13. German Hydrographic Institute, Hamburg
14. British National Institute of Oceanography
15. *Deep Sea Research*, Vol. 3, 1956
16. Scripps Institution of Oceanography
17. Bruce Heezen
18. Aircraft Operating Co. (Aerial Surveys), Johannesburg
19. Douglas P. Wilson, F.R.P.S.
20. Paleontological Research Institution, Ithaca, N.Y.
21. Geological Society of London
22. Nova Scotia Research Foundation
23. Valentine, Dundee
24. Spence Air Photos, Los Angeles
25. U.S. Information Service
26. Jack Worsley

The Lord possessed me in the beginning of his way, before his works of old.

I was set up from eternity, and of old, before the earth was made.

When there were no depths, I was brought forth, when there were no springs abounding with water.

Before the mountains were settled, before the hills was I brought forth:

He had not yet made the earth, nor the rivers, nor the poles of the world.

When he established the heavens, I was there, when he drew a circle on the face of the deep.

When he established the sky above, and poised the fountains of waters;

When he compassed the sea with its bounds, and set a law to the waters that they should not pass their limits:

Then I was beside him, like a master workman; and I was daily his delight, rejoicing before him always,

Rejoicing in the habitable part of his earth; and my delights were with the sons of men.

> Proverbs 8: 22–31 (22, 25, 31 – Authorised Version; 23, 26, 28, 29 – Douay Bible; 24, 27, 30 – Revised Version).

B

CHAPTER I

Crust, Mantle and Core

FIVE thousand million years ago the sun and its planets, of which the earth is one, were born as a spinning cloud of inter-stellar gas and stardust, out on a limb of our galaxy, the Milky Way.

Such is the testimony of the stars, as deciphered from their present colour and brightness by the astronomers. The infant sun was however very different from the blazing nuclear power station we recognise it to be today: even four thousand million years ago it was still only a ball of hydrogen and some heavier elements, its diameter that of the present orbit of Mercury, its temperature colder than ice. The surrounding planetary nebula was even colder; to be precise, more than two hundred degrees centigrade below the freezing point of water.

PROTO-EARTH

Now any such spinning cloud of cold gas-dust mixture is obliged to shrink to the form of a rotating disc. The shrinkage of the planetary nebula brought with it therefore an increase in material density which could locally override the gravitational authority of the already contracting central sun. The disc began to break up by local gravitational accretion into separate rotating clouds, the proto-planets, of which proto-earth was one – a clot of star-dust a little warmer than the pristine nebula, but still only some forty degrees centigrade above absolute zero.

Another 500 million years, and the sun began to shrink under the pull of its own gravity. And no sooner did its hydrogen atoms get together than up went its temperature. The shrinking sun, fed by the same potent nuclear processes which are all too familiar to mankind today in the hydrogen bomb, started to

19

transmit sunlight on its present visible and ultra-violet wavelengths. Consequently, the tenuous gas between the proto-planets was swept clean away by the new broom of the radiant sun, by the pressure of sunlight, just as today we can observe how the comets' tails are pushed outwards as they approach the sun.

Once interplanetary space had been swept clear by the nascent sun the now spherical proto-planets – including of course the earth – came under a fierce bombardment of atomic

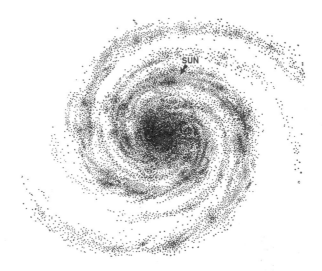

1.1. Our place in the sun, out on an arm of our spiral galaxy – the Milky Way.

particles – protons and electrons – and of the immaterial photons of visible and ultra-violet light, emitted by the sun: with the inevitable result that they forthwith proceeded to lose a greater or lesser proportion of their more volatile components by evaporation into the surrounding space.

And proto-earth, the greater part of its primeval gases gone with the solar wind, shrank to form a compact central ball of much the same chemical composition as the earth we live on today. The result was that it melted, under the combined effects of the release of gravitational energy which must follow any such contraction and of the heat generated by the entrapped radio-active elements.

Then, over a period of perhaps another 1,000 million years, came the gradual cooling of the white-hot earth by radiation into outer space, and a radial separation into a highly compressed central solid core, a liquid inner core, a semi-plastic mantle, and a primeval basaltic crust, the present phase of which is illustrated in Fig. 1.2.

Here the words 'present phase' are used advisedly: for the separation of the liquid nickel-iron core from the surrounding mantle has probably been a gradual process, which may indeed only now be entering on its final stage. Thus 3,000 million years ago the radius of the liquid core may well have been only a tenth of its present value: a supposition which will reveal itself as of fundamental importance in the sequel.

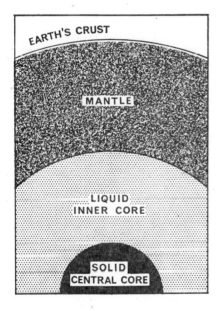

1.2. The interior of the earth as revealed by the earthquake-hunters: a central solid core, composition unknown, radius 800 miles; an inner core of nickel-iron, held molten at a temperature of 1,000°C under pressures of the order of a million atmospheres, outer radius 2,150 miles; a mantle of rock, olivine or serpentine in character, thickness 1,800 miles; and the crust we can explore from the surface.

EARTHQUAKES GALORE

The detailed knowledge of the interior structure of the earth, epitomised in Fig. 1.2, has been won, in the main over the past fifty years or so, from a systematic study of earthquakes. The prototype of the modern earthquake-hunter (or seismologist) is the Indian brave, listening with his ear to the ground for the approaching footfall of the enemy. In every scientifically developed country of the world there are 'listening posts': seismo-logical stations, equipped with sensitive seismographs which register the arrival – as earth tremors – of the seismic waves radiated in all directions from the point of origin, or focus, of each and every earthquake (see Plate IV).

Moreover, the earth is a lavish provider of earthquakes. Thus Kenneth Bullen of Sydney, Australia, acknowledged as one of the best earthquake-hunters in the world, estimates that in an average year ten earthquakes are national disasters, another hundred cause serious local destruction, a thousand do some damage, ten thousand give rise to alarm, one hundred thousand are felt as earth tremors by human beings, and many more are detectable only by the sensitive seismographs.

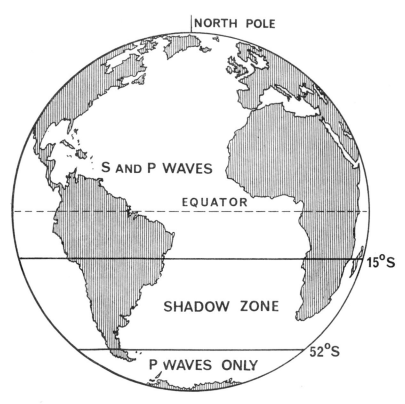

1.3. The pattern of P and S seismic waves received at the earth's surface from an earthquake having its focus in the mantle immediately below the north pole.

Seismic waves are of two kinds – longitudinal waves, which like sound waves depend on the *compressibility* of the medium which carries them; and transverse waves, which depend on its *elasticity*. These two different kinds of waves are known in the jargon of seismology as P waves and S waves respectively. P waves can travel through both solids and liquids, both of which are compressible; S waves can travel only through solids, because solids possess elastic properties, whereas liquids do not.

Like any other kind of wave, seismic waves are *refracted*, or bent, at the boundary between two different media. But whereas light waves, with which we are most familiar, travel more slowly in a dense medium, such as glass, than in a less dense medium like air, the reverse is the case for seismic waves. The result is that whereas light is deflected towards the base of a glass prism, a P wave would be deflected towards its apex.

Now suppose a major earthquake occurs at a point in the mantle lying beneath the North Pole. Seismographs stationed anywhere north of latitude 15°S. would record the arrival of both P and S waves; the more sensitive seismographs situated between 15°S. and 52°S. (including Bullen's at Sydney) would record very feeble P waves, but no S waves; while at those

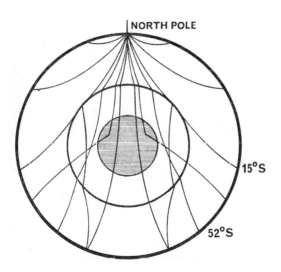

1.4. The shadow zone of Fig. 1.3, properly interpreted, leads immediately to the picture of the earth's interior illustrated in Fig. 1.2.

which lie south of 52 °S. the P waves would come in 'loud and clear' once more.

And now for the interpretation of the so-called 'shadow zone', which is a feature common to all earthquakes, no matter where their centres of activity may be located.

In the first place, the fade-out of the P waves inside the shadow zone means that they must have encountered a large central core in the interior of the earth in which their velocity is sharply reduced, causing them to be bent abruptly *inwards* at the boundary between the mantle in which they originated and the core. In the second place the total disappearance of the S waves at the margin of the shadow zone can only mean that the inner core is *liquid*; for, as we have seen, a liquid is ruled out as a medium for the propagation of S waves. And finally, the appearance of weak P waves *inside* the shadow zone reveals the presence of a *small solid core*, which bends the P waves *outwards* at its boundary.

BUILT-IN DYNAMO

Little more is known about the central solid core of the earth than its existence. It is quite otherwise, however, with the liquid inner core. Here the consensus of opinion is for a molten nickel-iron core under high pressure: for such a composition for the liquid inner core agrees well with the observed velocity of those earthquake P waves which traverse it, as also with the composition of meteorites – planetary fragments which have failed to coalesce by 'cold accretion' – which arrive on the earth's surface from interplanetary space. Moreover, it serves to explain the observed phenomena of the earth's magnetic field.

Now the first crucial fact about the so-called *total magnetic field* of the earth is that it lines up tolerably exactly with the earth's axis of rotation. This total magnetic field is, however, a complicated one, and it is therefore *resolved* for practical purposes into two main components: first, a *dipole field*, namely that which would belong to a gigantic bar magnet thrust through the globe, inclined at an angle of around 10° to the axis of rotation (see Fig. 1.5); and a *residual field*, which we shall discuss in the next section.

How then to interpret the total external magnetic field

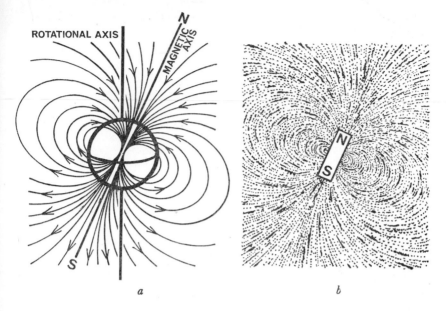

1.5. (a), (b). **To a first approximation, the magnetic field of the earth (a) is equivalent to that of a bar magnet (b).**

of the earth as arising from the properties of a molten nickel-iron core?

In recent years Bullard of Cambridge and Elsasser of La Jolla in California have suggested that the earth's magnetic field is that of a *self-exciting dynamo*, like that illustrated in Fig. 1.6, whose seat lies in the motions of the substance of the liquid inner core.

They argue that the heat transported outwards from the liquid inner core to the mantle and so outwards through the crust into space is to be accounted for, not only by *conduction*, but by *thermal convection* as well: that is, by the actual physical transport of the heated particles of the core radially from the outer boundary of the solid central core to the inner boundary of the mantle, and the return of the cooler particles from mantle to central core. In other words, they assume the existence of radially directed *convection cells* in the liquid inner core, and strive to match these with possible models of a 'homogeneous dynamo' which shall give rise to the observed external magnetic field of the earth.

25

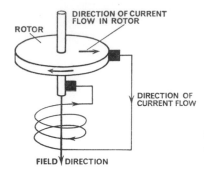

1.6. Here is a skeleton diagram of a self-exciting dynamo, such as is invoked in the liquid inner core to account for the earth's magnetic field.

And here we take our cue from a magistral scientific paper on the subject by Bullard and Gellman, published in the Philosophical Transactions of the Royal Society of London in 1954.

Bullard and Gellman begin by drawing attention to the differences which must exist between the engineer's self-exciting dynamo and the homogeneous dynamo of the earth's interior. In tabular form these differences are as follows:

Engineer's Dynamo	*Homogeneous Dynamo*
1. Solid material brushes.	Fluid 'brushes', realised by the liquid of the outer reaches of the core rotating against those nearer the centre.
2. Multiply connected.	Singly connected.
3. Coil has clockwise symmetry.	Coil has spheroidal symmetry.

Of these, the first two are trivial – the second in particular, because even an engineer's dynamo can function quite adequately when coil and disc are connected by a thin sheet of liquid.

The third difference, however, is crucial: for it is just the clockwise symmetry of the engineer's coil which causes the current to flow in such a direction as to produce a magnetic field which reinforces the initial field; whereas in the homogeneous dynamo of the earth's core any asymmetry can lie only *in the motion of its parts.*

The question of whether it is possible to think up a self-exciting dynamo as the begetter of the earth's magnetic field therefore boils down to this: Does an asymmetry of *motion* alone suffice to produce a dynamo, or is asymmetry of *structure* also necessary?

In analysing to this end the possible motions of the substance of the liquid core, we note to begin with that the thermal convection cells are disposed *ab initio* radially within the core – that is, *in meridianal planes*. Only *ab initio*, however; for gyroscopic forces soon force them to turn around into planes parallel to the equatorial plane, just as a gyro-compass is forced to rotate with its axis parallel to that of the earth.

There are numerous patterns in which the convection cells, thus stably oriented, could be arranged to give dynamo action. The simplest pattern is shown in Fig. 1.7(a), which illustrates the 'T2 pattern', or in the sophisticated language of the mathematical physicist 'the second toroidal mode'.

Concentrating now on the T2 pattern, we note that a highly conducting liquid under high pressure is subject to the laws of Magnetohydrodynamics: in plain language, that the magnetic lines of force in the earth's inner core are carried along with the moving particles of the fluid. Now the dipole field of the earth possesses *a radial component*, which moves with the liquid of the core across regions of differing speed of rotation: with the result that the lines of force curl themselves into tight spirals about the stream-lines of the T2 pattern.

And it must not be forgotten that these stream-lines also possess a latent radial component, since the *ab initio* direction

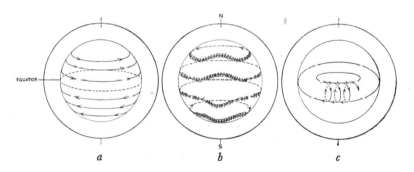

1.7.(a), (b), (c). Fig. 1.7(a) shows the simplest pattern of stream-lines in the inner liquid core which could foster a homogeneous dynamo – the so-called 'T2 pattern';

Fig. 1.7(b) illustrates the magnetic lines of force attached to the moving particles of the liquid core, coiled around the stream-lines of the T2 pattern, and distorted from the ideal of Fig. 1.7(a) by the motion;

Fig. 1.7(c) shows the resulting axial toroidal magnetic field, responsible for the external magnetic field of the earth (after Bullard and Gellman).

of the convection cells was itself radial. Consequently, the idealised T2 motion gets *distorted* into the pattern illustrated in Fig. 1.7(b). But here lies the final clue to the conundrum of the homogeneous dynamo; for it is in virtue of this very distortion that the resultant axial toroidal field illustrated in Fig. 1.7(c) is *self-maintaining* – without it, the enhanced field arising from the motion of the lines of force in a strict T2 pattern would merely dwindle away with time.

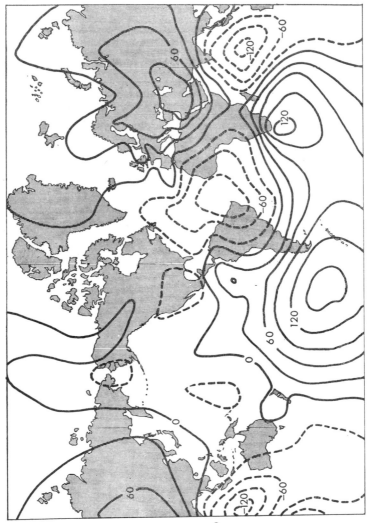

1.8. A world map of the vertical component of the local magnetic field for the period 1942 to 1945, reflecting the pattern of turbulent currents in the outer layers of the liquid inner core. The whole pattern drifts westward at the rate of about 12 miles per annum (after Vestine).

Bullard has therefore demonstrated that the earth's magnetic field can indeed be attributed to a homogeneous dynamo lodged in the earth's liquid inner core. This is not to say, however, that the dynamo mechanism is the only possible one; nor even then that the T2 pattern of fluid flow is the only pattern which could give rise to dynamo action. Nevertheless, comparison of the earth's magnetic field with say that of sunspots, where 'bottled magnetism' seems to offer the only possible explanation, leads us to rank the homogeneous dynamo mechanism very high as a working hypothesis in the understanding of the origins of the earth's magnetic field.

SURFACE EDDIES

Next, we examine the conditions which must exist at the boundary between the inner liquid core and its semi-solid sheath, where the T2 equatorial stream-lines brush the inner surface of the mantle.

As with any stream-lined flow of a liquid completely filling a solid container, we must expect to find *turbulent eddy-currents* in the outer layers of the liquid. And so indeed we do in the

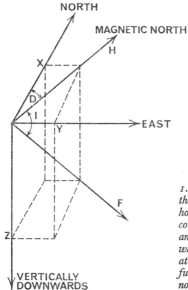

1.9. The local magnetic field F at any point in the northern hemisphere, decomposed into its horizontal component H and its vertical component Z. Note that F is inclined to H at an angle I (the magnetic inclination, or dip), which is determined by the latitude: being zero at the equator and 90° at the pole. Note further that H differs in direction from true north by the angle D, the so-called declination.

case of the liquid inner core – eddy-currents which reveal themselves at the earth's surface as local perturbations of the axial field of the steady toroidal currents in the core. A glance at Fig. 1.8, in which Vestine of Minneapolis in the United States has charted the vertical component of the local magnetic field at different places on the globe, convinces one immediately of the truth of that statement.

Vestine's maps of the earth's local magnetic field (i.e., axial field plus 'residual field'), of which our Fig. 1.8 is only one of many examples, are sharply reminiscent of the weather maps of the meteorologists – all the more so as the whole pattern is found to be drifting westwards, like clouds across a summer sky, at the rate of some 12 miles per annum.

Now this can only mean that crust and mantle are rotating from west to east at a greater speed than the core. And the reason is not far to seek: the inner mantle, composed as it is predominantly of iron-magnesium silicates, is a fair conductor of electricity. This means that core and mantle are electrically coupled, to the extent that the eddy-currents at the surface of the liquid core can leak into the substance of the lower mantle. The mantle thus becomes as it were the armature of an electric motor of which the field is the axial field of the earth, and so is driven eastward relative to the core; and we, as observers perched on the solid crust-mantle surface of the earth, interpret our eastward motion as a westward motion of the core and its eddy currents.

WRITTEN IN THE STARS

When Candlemas comes round again, boys who live in the Auld Toon of Edinboro' or the Gallowgate of Aberdeen still bring their whipping tops out onto the pavement. They call their tops 'peeries', a term borrowed, as with many another civilised custom of the Scots, off their one-time allies, in the French word 'pirouette'.

Fig. 1.10 is a portrait of a typical peerie, nicely fashioned on a wood-turner's lathe, grooves for the whip and all. Flung outwards and downwards off the encircling cord of the whip, it lands on the pavement: and the odds are hundreds to one that its axis is inclined to the vertical when it starts to spin. It strives to spin upright, but has to compromise, at least for a start, by

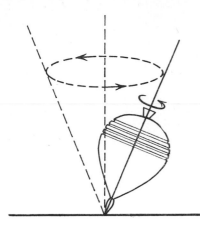

1.10. The child's whipping top reproduces quite faithfully the precession and nutation in space of the earth's axis.

precessing about the vertical, and in so doing describes the so-called *space-cone*, whose apex coincides with the point of the top.

Moreover, it inevitably encounters transient side-pressures in the shape of bumps and hollows in the pavement, or of cracks between paving stones. These transients set up a *nutation* about the axis of the top itself whereby, precessing the while, the axis of rotation describes a *body-cone*, which rolls on the imaginary surface of the space-cone with a free period of nutation characteristic of the particular top in question. As time marches on, the *friction* between the point of the top and the pavement brings the axis of rotation into the vertical, in which position the friction is a minimum. The top sleeps – or in the vernacular 'snores'. It's not every top that will snore, and it's a proud wee boy whose top snores soonest – to be lashed on the instant with his whip. And the whole cycle repeats itself, for hours of a bright spring morning.

Here not for the first time the child is father of the man: for we have come to learn that our own earth is a top, spinning in space as it circles the sun, its axis of rotation precessing about the vertical to the plane of its orbit with a period of 26,000 years, sweeping out a cone in space having a semi-vertical angle of $23\frac{1}{2}°$. And because there is no friction on the point of a top spinning in space, that angle is held steady to all eternity.

The terrestrial top is forced into this precession by the torque which arises from the gravitational attraction of the sun and moon acting on the bulge of the earth at the Equator. But, just like the peerie, the earth's axis of rotation describes its own little body-cone in space, rolling on the space-cone as it precesses. This second motion of the earth's axis is a two-component 'free nutation', triggered by two separate mechanisms: first, a nutation having a period of 14 months, set off by the seasonal variation in the distribution of snow and ice, and of the atmosphere itself, between the northern and the southern hemispheres; and second a nutation having very nearly a diurnal period, triggered by the earth-tides in the crust and mantle. Let us look at these two periods of nutation, which together decide the angle of the body-cone, rather more closely.

To begin with, we recall that back in 1758 the great German mathematician, Euler, had analysed in complete detail the motions of a rigid spinning top; and proved that if the terrestrial top were a rigid body its period of free nutation should be 10 months. Then came S. C. Chandler of Cambridge (Mass.) who showed, from an analysis of the observed variations in the latitude of a number of places on the earth's surface over the period 1840 to 1891, that the period of free nutation of the terrestrial top was not 10, but 14 months. The reason is that the crust and mantle of the earth are *not* rigid. They possess *elastic properties*, as is evidenced above all in the phenomena of isostasy which we shall meet with later in Chapter 2.

And now, in 1963, Nikolai Popov of the Poltava Gravimetrical Observatory in the Ukraine has demonstrated that the free nutation having a near diurnal period arises from the spontaneous compression and decompression of *the earth's liquid core*, triggered off by the transient effect of the earth tides in its retaining shell.

Popov has established this very important fact as the result of a laborious observation of two bright stars in the zenith of the firmament—a Persei and η Ursa Major. Here he reverts in a measure to the methods of the Egyptian priest-scientists of the IVth Dynasty, who knew something of the precession, as distinct from the nutation, of the terrestrial top: for it is a fact that the sloping shafts of the Great Pyramid are most cunningly constructed so as to allow an exact observation by the dead Pharaoh of the star a Draconis, to which the earth's axis pointed 4,000 years ago, where today it points to our Pole Star, a in Ursa Minor. In like manner, Popov has pointed his Zeiss zenith telescope, ever since 1939, night and day over the

32

years, alternately at η Ursa Major and α Persei as they replaced one another approximately every 12 hours at the zenith; and so has determined the shorter period of free nutation as 23 hours 56 minutes 54 seconds, with the incredible accuracy of 4 parts in a thousand. And this is precisely the period predicted by his fellow countryman Nikolai Pariinsky from his analysis of the triggering effect of the earth tides in crust and mantle on the free period of oscillation of a liquid nickel-iron core under compression.

So the Soviet astronomers have come to the aid of the Commonwealth seismologists: the interior of the earth is indeed that of our Fig. 1.2 – and we should hear rather less of cores of compressed hydrogen or the second ultraphase of an ultrabasic silicate mass.

EARTH'S MANTLE

The density of the liquid iron core, as deduced from the speed at which the seismic waves radiating from earthquake centres travel in it, as also from Popov's new results, is about twice that of the surrounding mantle, which is most probably composed of iron-magnesium silicate rock, similar to the basaltic mineral olivine. When the earth first melted, core and mantle would have existed as a magma of liquid iron and iron silicates, from which the liquid iron gradually separated, much as in an industrial blast furnace: a process of separation which, as already stressed, is perhaps even yet not fully complete.

The mantle is the seat of the deep-focus earthquakes that tell us what we know of the interior of the earth; its outer zone is the source of the lavas that are the primordial constituent of continents and ocean islands; earth's volcanoes are the vents for the release of its volcanic gases, which metamorphosed give us the air we breathe; the seven seas were almost certainly once literally 'waters under the earth', hidden as 'juvenal water' in the mantle. In short, the mantle is of supreme importance in the shaping of earth's surface features: the mountains of the continental rafts; the coral atolls of the Pacific; the majestic topography of the ocean floor; even the overall pattern of land and sea – all have the stamp of the mantle upon them. Some of these products of the mantle are illustrated in Plates II and III.

c

Once the first bold outline of the mantle had been traced by the seismic waves from deep-focus earthquakes, the seismologists could proceed to a closer examination of its structure. Thus it is clear from a glance at Fig. 1.4 that the longer is the travel time between earthquake focus and observation station, the deeper is the level at which the seismic waves from that focus have made their way through the substance of the mantle. If then the substance of the mantle were uniform throughout its depth, the travel time would be uniformly proportional to the distance between the source of the earthquake and its point of detection at the earth's surface. However, it turns out that this is not the case.

In the first place, the travel times for waves that have passed through the lower levels of the mantle are found to be *less* than would be predicted from a constant proportionality between distance travelled in the mantle and travel time. In other words, the substance of the mantle near its boundary with the inner liquid core is *denser* than the average. This is of course exactly what we should expect to find if the separation of metallic iron and silicate rock at or near the inner boundary is not yet complete.

In the second place, the earlier workers found another break in the uniform proportionality between travel time and distance travelled: namely, when source and seismograph were at an angular distance of some 20° apart, which came to be called in the jargon of seismology 'the 20° discontinuity'. In this case, however, the travel time was *greater* than the average: in other words, the velocity of propagation of seismic waves was *less* than the average.

The so-called '20° discontinuity' was analysed with particular care by the late Beno Gutenberg of Pasadena in California, on the basis of seismograph records of earthquakes originating in four different areas – Japan, the Mediterranean, Rumania and India. He expressed his results as indicating a layer in the upper mantle at a depth between 100 and 200 kilometres below its upper boundary, in which the velocity of the P waves dropped from the customary 8·2 km/sec to 7·85 km/sec, and that of S waves from 4·6 km/sec to 4·4 km/sec: in short a layer in which the substance of the mantle is *less viscous and more plastic* than at levels either above or below it.

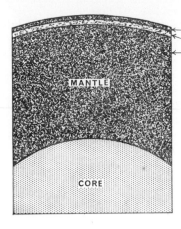

←Vp = 8·2 km sec
←Vp = 7·85 km sec
←Vp ~ 8 km sec

1.11. Illustrating the 'Gutenberg channel' in the upper mantle – a layer of lower viscosity and greater plasticity than the average, which allows the movement of extensive portions of the crust relative to each other and to the underlying mantle.

Gutenberg's conclusions, reached as the result of a laborious analysis of the travel times and amplitudes of seismic waves radiating from the foci of natural earthquakes, have been confirmed directly by the observation of these same quantities for seismic waves originating from underground explosions of atomic bombs in the Nevada desert. Quantitatively, the more precise delineation of the Gutenberg low velocity layer made possible by such direct experiment gives the vertical span of the layer as between 60 and 150 kilometres below surface.

Moreover, recent studies of *surface waves* from atomic explosions – seismic waves which travel in the crust but 'feel' the substrata to a depth of the same order as their own wavelength – show that the low velocity layer is of global extent lying hidden beneath the surface of land and sea alike.

MAY 22 1960

The 'Gutenberg channel' remained, however, largely in the realm of theoretical deduction until the date of the Chile earthquake of May 22 1960, which not only sent a great tidal wave sweeping across the Pacific to New Zealand and Japan, but also made the whole globe of the earth literally 'ring like a bell'. The fact that seismographs capable of directly recording the deep seismic notes of the earth's bell were already installed at two separate stations – at Isabella, California, and at Palisades, New York – is due primarily to Gutenberg's pupil, Hugo Benioff.

35

Benioff had detected an oscillatory movement with a period of over 50 minutes in the records of the Kamchatka earthquake of November 4 1952, which he – rightly, as it turned out – attributed to a fundamental oscillation of the earth as a whole. Both he and Maurice Ewing of New York thereupon set out to build special long-period seismographs which could record precisely and directly such very long-period vibrations. At the same time, the theoreticians got busy with some highly com-

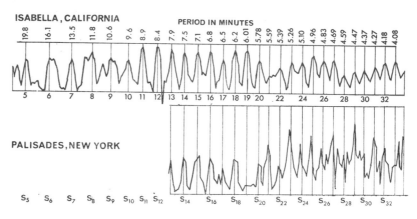

1.12. The great Chile earthquake of May 22 1960: overtones of the fundamental mode of vibration S1 of the earth as a spherical bell, observed simultaneously on the seismometers at Isabella, California, and Palisades, New York, compared with those predicted on the Bullen-Gutenberg model of the earth's interior (after Benioff and Ewing).

plicated calculations, made possible only with the aid of modern high-speed electronic computers, which should predict not only the fundamental tone, but also the long series of overtones, which would fit the natural modes of vibration of several possible 'earth models' – including that of Bullen–Gutenberg.

So when the catastrophe of the Chile earthquake occurred, the coldly impersonal Benioff seismographs at Isabella and Palisades duly recorded the great bell of the earth ringing out the awful news: a deep fundamental vibration of period 53·9 minutes, and a whole series of overtones ranging from 19·8 minutes right up the scale of 32 steps to 4·08 minutes – and each and every one matched by the corresponding overtone predicted by the theoreticians *on the basis of the Bullen–Gutenberg model of the mantle.*

Thus at a single stroke the actual existence of the thirty-year-old Gutenberg hypothesis of a layer of minimum viscosity and maximum plasticity in the upper portion of the mantle was established beyond a peradventure. Large-scale movements of portions of the earth's crust relative to the mantle, either vertically in the formation of continental rafts, or horizontally in continental drift or in transcurrent faulting of the ocean floor, the possibility of which has been so hotly debated in the past, now find their natural locus in the plastic Gutenberg channel: topics which are dealt with at length in succeeding chapters of this book.

THE EARTH'S CRUST

The primordial crust of the earth is a skin of serpentine basaltic rock some 5 miles thick, lying atop the mantle to form both the ocean floor and the foundation of the continental rafts of granitic rocks, themselves 20 to 25 miles in thickness.

That is a bald statement of the facts, as established by a study of shallow-focus or 'near' earthquakes on the one hand; and by 'seismic shooting' with man-made explosives, both on land and at sea, on the other.

Harold Jeffreys, in his classic book *The Earth*, says: "Technically a near earthquake is one well observed at a number of stations near enough to record P and S waves in the granitic upper layer, that is, within about 6° (i.e., of earth's arc). It is usually a small earthquake, because in a large one at small distances the movement is too violent for anything but the first displacement to be read."

Possibly the most fruitful of all near earthquakes occurred on the morning of October 8 1909, about 40 kilometres south of Zagreb, where Dr. Andrija Mohorovičić (pronounced Mohoŕro-vich-ich) was director of the meteorological observatory. Mohorovičić examined the seismograph records of the quake, not only those obtained at Zagreb, but others from stations all over Europe, and was led to the fundamentally important discovery of the 'Mohorovičić discontinuity' – an abrupt change in structure and material as between crust and underlying mantle.

The essence of Mohorovičić's discovery was the identification on his seismograph records of the arrival of not only one, but

37

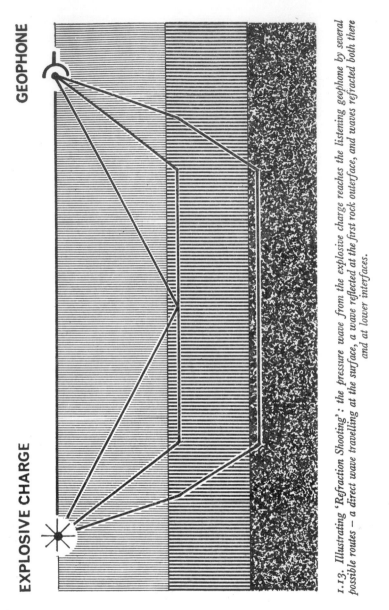

GEOPHONE

EXPLOSIVE CHARGE

1.13. Illustrating 'Refraction Shooting': the pressure wave from the explosive charge reaches the listening geophone by several possible routes – a direct wave travelling at the surface, a wave reflected at the first rock outerface, and waves refracted both there and at lower interfaces.

two P waves – the slower P wave having a velocity of about 6 km/sec, the faster one of 8·2 km/sec. (see Plate V). He boldly suggested that the slower P wave had followed the direct route from the focus of the near earthquake to his seismograph –

that is, through the comparatively light-weight granites of the crust; while the faster P wave had travelled by refraction through the denser material of the upper mantle. On the basis of this hypothesis, he gave a first rough estimate of the thickness of the continental crust in the European area as 50 kilometres.

Mohorovičić's interpretation of his observations is now widely accepted, although quantitatively his figure of 50 kilometres for the crustal thickness was something of an over-estimate – 30 to 45 kilometres, depending on the particular location, is now the currently accepted figure. However, 'Mohorovičić' has proved to be such a mouthful that his discontinuity – the boundary between crust and mantle – is universally known in the literature as 'the Moho'.

'Refraction shooting' with man-made explosives is now an accepted technique for the exploration of the earth's crust, particularly at sea. Here the experimenter has the obvious advantage of a precise knowledge of the time and place of his miniature earthquake. Usually the amount of explosive used is quite small – of the order of hundredweights rather than tons – although isolated advantage has been taken to record the seismic waves sent out for example from the gigantic post-war explosion in 1947 of the ammunition dump on the island of Heligoland, or a year later in the underground war factory of Haslach in the Black Forest, or from the underground detonation of atomic bombs in the Nevada desert. All alike give the same answer – a crustal sheath of basaltic rock some 5 miles thick beneath land and sea alike, P wave velocity 6·7 km/sec,

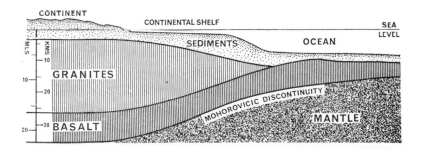

1.14. A generalised picture of the structure of the earth's crust: a global sheath of basaltic rock, overlaid either by the sediments atop the ocean floor, or by the granitic rafts of the continents, floating like great icebergs in the substance of the mantle.

39

overlaid on land by a continental upper crust of granites, gneisses, and schists 20 to 25 miles in thickness, P wave velocity around 6 km/ sec.

ISOSTASY

The basalt layer, which may well represent the earth's first primitive crust, must not be thought of as a geometrically perfect shell about the mantle, on which are piled the continents and the ocean sediments. Far from it. There are deep depressions in the floor of the oceans – the deep-sea trenches of a later chapter – below which the basalt layer is thinned out; while the same layer beneath the continents is buckled downwards, particularly below mountainous areas or beneath regions such as Greenland or Antarctica which are weighed down by an ice-cap. Under mountainous areas the basalt layer may either follow the profile of the peaks far above it, or may be so thickened that it actually offers a convex surface to the earth's interior; while the rise of the ground in areas such as Scandinavia, only recently released from the glaciation of the Pleistocene era, at the rate of a metre or more per century, is a well-established fact.

Such adjustments of the earth's crust are a consequence of 'isostasy', a term introduced by the American geologist Clarence Edward Dutton in 1892 to express the tendency of the crust towards *hydrostatic equilibrium*. The continents 'float' on the mantle, like icebergs in the sea; while the floors of the ocean trenches are sucked down into the mantle to float in it like sunken logs below the surface of a lake.

All this detailed information about the structure of the crust above the Moho has been obtained from place to place on the globe by a combination of measurements of gravity, rock densities, and seismic velocities, from which the thin floor of an ocean trench or the deep roots of a mountain range are deduced by often laborious computation.

Hence the next phase in the exploration of the Moho is to drill a hole right down through the discontinuity and to bring up samples of rock from levels lying both above and below it. Preliminary work on this bold enterprise has indeed already been accomplished, in trials near the island of Guadalupe, off the west coast of Mexico.

The opening chapters of the story of the Guadalupe venture are slightly farcical. The characters involved, in order of their appearance, are Hess and Munk of the Scripps Oceanographic Institution at La Jolla; AMSOC – short for The American Miscellaneous Society – a gang of U.S. earth scientists formed 'to encourage miscellaneous projects', not a few of them deliberately far-fetched; and Sir Edward Bullard and such of his colleagues as were present at the big meeting of the International Union of Geodesy and Geophysics at Toronto in the fall of 1957.

Hess and Munk made their proposal for a 'Mohole' to AMSOC in the spring; Bullard took up the challenge in the autumn at Toronto, and talked the Union into passing a formal resolution in support of what the majority considered to be a crack-brained project (see Plates V and VI).

'Came the dawn' ... The U.S. National Science Foundation in Washington took over from AMSOC, appointed Dr. Willard Bascom as co-ordinator, and proceeded to spend three million dollars on the job.

The preliminary results are extremely promising: the AMSOC/NSF Mohole Committee chartered the sea-going barge CUSS I, owned by the Continental, Union, Shell and Superior Oil Companies, sited her off the island of Guadalupe, where the water is only 3,760 metres deep above the 5-kilometre-thick basalt floor of the ocean, positioned her between four totally submerged radar-sonar buoys moored to the ocean floor by stout steel wires, and with the aid of a lone steersman seated before a radar screen, on which the position of the buoys appeared as four bright spots, kept her there by means of a single handle controlling four propellers located at the four corners of the barge.

Drilling with a diamond bit held co-axially at the lower end of a string of drill pipes – restrained from uncontrolled bending and consequent fracture as the barge pitched and rolled, in winds as much as 30 miles an hour and seas over 10 feet high, by a conical guide placed around the uppermost 50 feet or so of drill pipe – could then begin.

The bit ground out a hollow cylinder of rock, the core of which was pushed up inside an inner tube held axially in the bottom section of the drill pipe. This inner tube could then be raised to the surface, core and all, for subsequent examination, without disturbing the drill-pipe and bit.

In this first trial boring, 180 metres of sediment overlying the basalt floor of the ocean were penetrated, some 15 metres of the basalt floor itself. The cores are now being examined for chemical composition and age. The next step is the 'Mohole' proper.

UMP

The Mohole, however, will be only one of a whole series of observations of the earth's mantle scheduled for the so-called International Upper Mantle Project 1964 ('UMP' for short). The proposal to extend the Mohole project, first proposed at Toronto in 1957, to include a major concerted attack on the nature of the upper mantle, came from V. V. Beloussov of the USSR at the 1960 General Assembly of the Geophysics Union, held at Helsinki in Finland. The Union adopted a formal resolution recommending *inter alia*: Deep drilling, on land as well as at sea; the development of deep-sea seismographs for the exploration of the upper mantle under the oceans; special studies of deep focus earthquakes; magnetic and gravimetric studies of the upper mantle; high pressure laboratory studies of the behaviour of rocks.

The recommendations of the Union have been endorsed by its parent organisation, the International Council of Scientific Unions; and an international committee is now directing the operational phase of the campaign. Hess and Munk of La Jolla, California, and Bullard and Maurice Hill of Cambridge, England, may well have the last laugh.

CHAPTER 2

Mountain Building

WHEN the liquid nickel-iron core separated out from the silicate rocks of the mantle, between three and four thousand million years ago, the bulk of the radio-active elements, such as uranium and thorium, were left behind in the mantle. Too bulky to fit well into the crystal pattern of the constituents of the mantle, they began to work their way outwards towards the crust. Today the radio-active elements are concentrated mainly in the crust, possibly in the upper reaches of the mantle; but particularly in the granitic rocks of the continental rafts.

RADIO-ACTIVE CLOCKS

Now all radio-active substances decay, by the steady spontaneous disintegration of the nuclei of the atoms of which they are composed, into substances which are non-radio-active. The classic example is the decay of uranium, via a whole chain of radio-active elements, into the non-radio-active substance lead. If then a sample of uranium-bearing rock is taken and analysed for the amount of lead end-product which has been produced

TABLE 2.1: Radio-active isotopes used in age determinations

Parent Isotope	End-product	Half-life (millions of years)
Uranium-238	Lead-206	4,510
Thorium-232	Lead-208	13,900
Potassium-40	Argon-40	11,850
	Calcium-40	1,470
Rubidium-87	Strontium-87	47,000

43

from its parent, the age of the rock is determined from the known rate of decay of the uranium atoms.

In Table 2.1 are assembled a number of naturally occurring radio-active substances, the clocks which are used to determine the age of the rocks forming the earth's crust.

Two definitions are needed in the study of this Table. First, an 'isotope', as its name implies, is an elementary atomic species occupying the same place in the Periodic Table of the elements as one or more others. This becomes clear if for example we write the radio-active atomic disintegration series for Uranium and Thorium across the bottom of Mendeleef's Periodic Table of the chemical elements, as has been done in Fig. 2.1.

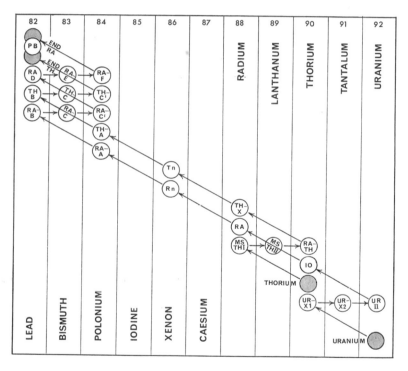

2.1. *The atomic disintegration series of Uranium and Thorium written across the face of the Periodic Table. Both series terminate in the birth of atoms of non-radioactive lead – atomic weight 206 for Uranium lead, 208 for thorium lead ('ordinary' lead weighs 204 on the atomic weight scale). The numbers 82 to 92 are the so-called 'atomic numbers' of the elements, which begin with 1 for hydrogen. Look particularly at atomic number 84 – here there are as many as five radio-active atomic species isotopic with Polonium.*

44

Second, the 'half-life' of a radio-active substance is the time taken for half the amount originally present to decay, through the spontaneous radio-active disintegration of its atomic nuclei, as illustrated in Fig. 2.2.

A glance at Fig. 2.1 shows us that there are at least two species of lead, the non-radio-active end products of the Uranium and Thorium disintegration series. Hence we are allowed at least two independent shots at determining the age of uranium- or thorium-bearing deposits, by analysing them

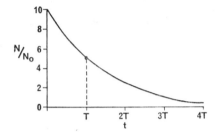

2.2. *Illustrates the exponential decay of a sample of a radio-active substance by spontaneous nuclear disintegration. N_0 is the number of atoms originally present in the sample; N is the number of atoms remaining untransmuted after a lapse of time t; and T is the 'half-life', for which $N/N_0 = 0.5$.*

with the aid of the mass spectrograph for the ratios U238: Pb206; and for Th232:Pb208 -- since from measurements made in the laboratory we know the rate of decay and 'half-life' of the radio-active substances U238 and Th232. A control is also available for the quantity of 'common' lead, not of radio-active origin, which may and usually is present in uranium-bearing pitch-blende or thorium-rich monazite sand, in the determination of the amount of Pb204 present, since this isotope of lead is not a product of the radio-active decay of heavier elements.

In this way, remarkably accurate determinations can be made of the age of a surprisingly large number of rocks. The scope of geological age determination has however been vastly increased in the past decade by the development of the two remaining methods featured in Table 2.1, namely the Argon-40: Potassium-40 method; and the Strontium-87: Rubidium-87 method, since Potassium-40 in particular is the constituent of many rock-forming minerals of all ages. Micas give particularly valuable results, since the volatile gas argon is held firmly in its atomic form in the natural crystal lattice, particularly of biotite, muscovite and lepidolite micas.

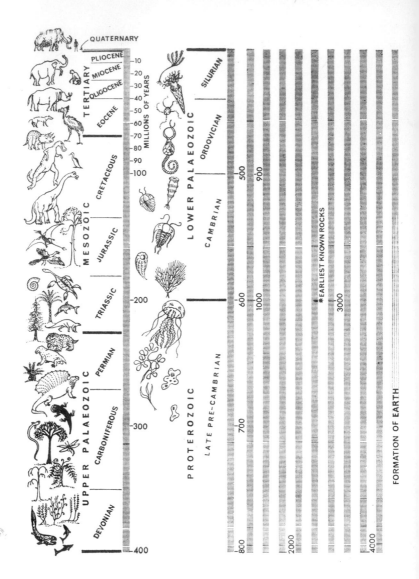

2.3. The geological column of six eras and fourteen periods, the dates of which in the world's history book are recorded by radio-active clocks preserved in successive strata of the earth's crust.

And here in Fig. 2.3 is the modern geological column which results, to which we shall frequently refer in the sequel.

The age of the oldest rocks in the geological column, as determined by radio-active dating, is around 3,000 million years – in excellent agreement incidentally with the astronomical estimate. These are the ancient continental nuclei, such as are found uncovered by later deposits in Canada south of Hudson Bay, north of the Black Sea in the Ukraine, south of the Deccan plateau in India, and in the gold-fields of Western Australia.

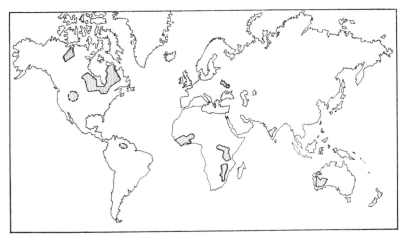

2.4. The ancient continental shields of the Pre-Cambrian era (after Tuzo Wilson).

These primitive continental shields are made up of both sedimentary and volcanic rocks, with a high preponderance of volcanic types – pillow lavas and basalts – which are never found repeated on the same scale in later formations. How then shall we decipher the first chapter of geological history, the formation of the gigantic mountains of which the continental nuclei are the seventh age? Perhaps the most fruitful approach to this problem is to look first with Tuzo Wilson of Toronto at the *youngest* mountains in the world – the island arcs of the China seas.

ISLAND ARCS

Spin a terrestrial globe so that you are faced with the Pacific Ocean, and you will see strung out before you, off the eastern shores of Asia, a long chain of islands, threaded like beads on a string from the Aleutians in the north to the island of Celebes in the south. Look closer, and observe that here is a necklace of *linked circular arcs*, concave towards the land, each one of them bordered on the seaward side by a deep trench in the ocean floor: the Aleutian trench, the Kuril trench, the Japanese trench, the Philippine trench.

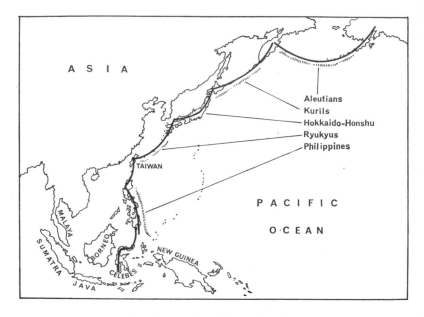

2.5. Island arcs and trenches in the China Seas.

These abyssal trenches of the Pacific are deep gashes in the earth's crust. The deepest of them, the Marianas trench, has been sounded by the USSR oceanographic vessel *Vitiaz* at 36,173 feet – deeper than Mount Everest is high. Gravity surveys, made by swinging a pendulum in an ocean-going submarine navigating the dead calm waters beneath the waves, reveal very large 'negative anomalies' beneath such trenches. In other words, the force of gravity is here way below its average value, which can only mean that the floors of the trenches lie far beneath the average level of the earth's crust – as if they had been sucked down under lateral compression into the substance of the upper mantle.

48

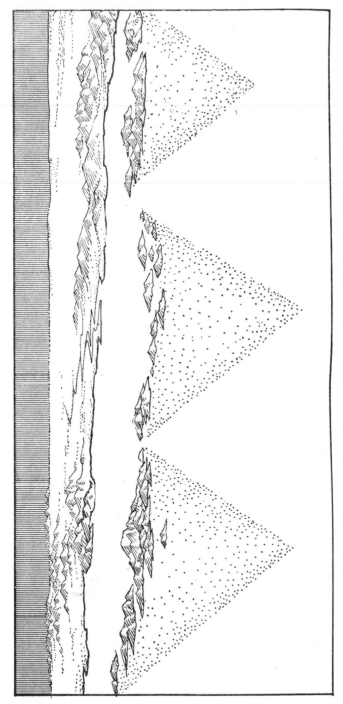

2.6. Cones of fracture in the earth's crust, which are at the root of the formation of the abyssal trenches and shoreward of these the volcanic island-arcs.

D

Earthquake studies tell the same tale: for beneath each and every ocean trench are the foci of shallow earthquakes originating in the upper mantle. Follow these shallow foci downwards, and you find not only shallow but deep earthquake foci, all lying on the surface of a cone whose apex lies 400 miles or more below the continental margin of East Asia. Moreover, such observational data are confirmed by a theoretical analysis of the fracture of a crust under compression, lying above a mantle in tension: an analysis which leads as in Fig. 2.7 to

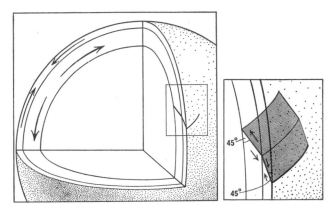

2.7. *Shows how compressional stresses in the earth's crust, above an upper mantle under tensional stress, lead by faulting to arctuate splits in the crust (after Scheidegger).*

just such a conical zone of fracture as would result in the formation of an arctuate ocean trench where the cone cuts the surface.

The island arcs which lie shoreward of the trenches are invariably volcanic in origin: they are formed of so-called *andesitic* lavas; lavas, that is, which carry a relatively high content of silica, in contrast to the purely basaltic lavas of which isolated mid-ocean islands are formed. Here the lavas of the island arcs betray their sub-continental origin: they have come upwards from the mantle through the continental crust to find the zone of crustal fracture defined by the trenches. In fact the whole surface geology of the Pacific basin is governed by the so-called *andesite line*, shoreward of which the lavas are of the continental type, a line which follows closely the seaward boundary of the chain of island arcs.

Follow now the line of island arcs you have looked at in the China Seas right around the globe. First, note that the chain branches at the island of Celebes: one branch thrusts eastward via New Guinea to the Solomon Islands, the New Hebrides and the North Island of New Zealand; while the other swings westward via the Java trench, then disappears beneath the waters of the Bay of Bengal, to reappear as the deep, deep valley of the Ganges, bordered on the north or continental side by the majestic ex-island arc of the Himalayas; then via the mountain arcs of Persia and of Turkey to the Dolomites of the Adriatic and the Apennines of Italy.

Next, retrace your steps northward from Celebes, up past the Philippines, Japan, the Kurils, the Aleutians: then over the top of the world to Alaska, and away south along the coastal mountains of British Columbia and the United States to the Andes of South America.

You have traced out on your globe a gigantic letter T, which marks the line along which splits in the earth's crust have made, or indeed are still being made, to form a world-wide compressional zone of linked conical fractures. See here Fig. 2.8.

AGE GROUPS

The arctuate formations which together form the great compressional fracture zone of the earth's crust are not all of the same age – far from it. Thus for example the island arcs of the China seas are about 150 million years of age, the Andes 250 million years, the Sierra Nevada and Cascade mountains of the western United States 400 million years; and once this difference in age among the different systems of mountain arcs is appreciated, the idea of an *evolutionary process* at work in mountain building becomes clamant.

Thus in the single island arcs of the Pacific we are witnessing the primary stage of mountain building at a continental margin; in the Andes we see the full formation of a primary mountain arc, as part of its continent; while the Sierra Nevada/ Cascade mountain chain is one member of a double mountain arc, the other being the Coastal Range of the western United States.

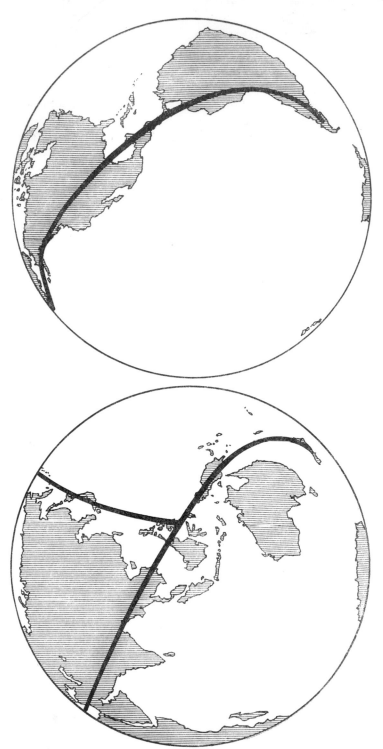

2.8. *The great T which the zone of compressional fracture in the earth's crust traces on the globe.*

The formation of a double mountain arc is the natural consequence of the initial juxtaposition of island arc and ocean trench. With the passage of time, the trench is gradually filled with sediments arising from the erosion of the volcanic peaks of the island arc; then comes the upthrust of the crust seaward required to maintain the overall balance of the load on the underlying mantle.

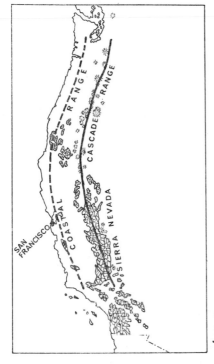

2.9. *The Sierra Nevada and Coastal Range of California: an example of the formation of a double mountain arc (after Tuzo Wilson).*

There are many examples of such double mountain arcs, apart from the Sierra Nevada/Coastal Range system in the United States – above all, in the series of five double arcs stretching westwards from Celebes on the east-west arm of the great T. Of these again, the most dramatic is the Himalayan double arc, facing south to the Indian subcontinent – where in Pre-Cretaceous times there rolled the ancient Tethys Sea.

53

Pinpointing once again the Sierra Nevada and the Cascade Mountains, together with the British Columbian coastal mountains lying to the north, we observe that they form a two-linked chain of circular arcs, with their *convex* aspect towards the coast; and further, that opposite the junction of these two arcs lies the curved bow of the Rocky Mountains, some two hundred miles inland, presenting its *concave* aspect to the coast.

Here in the Rockies is a typical example of a *secondary mountain arc*, thrown up by faulting in the cover rocks lying inland of the primary arcs: faults or 'lineaments' which spring from the area of strain in the crust where two conical fractures meet. Of the many other secondary arcs bordering 'the great T' we mention the Alps, the Caucasus, the Pamirs, and the

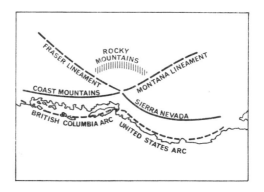

2.10. An example of the formation of a secondary mountain arc (after Tuzo Wilson).

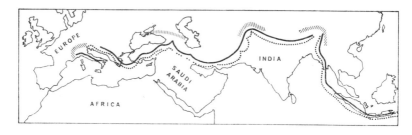

2.11. The festoon of primary and secondary mountain arcs which hangs on the east-west arm of the great T (after Tuzo Wilson).

mountains of the Burma Road: all formed on the continental side of the junctions between the five great primary arcs of the east-west fracture zone stretching from Celebes to the Strait of Gibraltar, and all with their concave faces looking south; or rather less dramatically, in the Puna Ridge of Bolivia, inland from the Andes and again concave to the coast; or in the embryonic secondary arcs of Western Kamchatka, the south island of Japan, and of Formosa – children of the youngest of all primary arcs, the island arcs of the China Seas.

ACTIVE AND INACTIVE

All the mountain ranges so far considered are classed as 'active', a term which includes the active volcanoes of the East Asian island arcs, the earthquake belt of the Andes, the all but quiescent Sierra Nevada, the still upthrusting mountains of the southern Eurasian belt. As inactive are classed such mountain systems as the great Appalachian system of North America; the still older Laurentian mountains in Canada, the Scottish Grampians, the Scandinavian shield; and of course the primeval continental nuclei.

Can we then trace on their wrinkled faces the heyday of a youth spent as an active mountain arc? The answer is: Yes, if we look closely enough.

THE APPALACHIANS

The Appalachians, the major mountain system of the eastern United States, are a prime example of an inactive mountain range of comparatively recent age. Their rocks date from Paleozoic times, around 400 million years ago, as compared with the oldest rocks of the Pre-Cambrian era, aged some 3,000 million years. Yet they are quite inactive, in the sense that both volcanism and earthquakes are completely absent; and one asks oneself immediately whether there is any evidence that they once formed part of a system of active mountain arcs: in other words, whether they represent today a later stage than say the Andes in an evolutionary process of mountain building and continental growth.

Now the earliest systematic survey of the geology of the United States traced a narrow chain of seven linked 'salients'

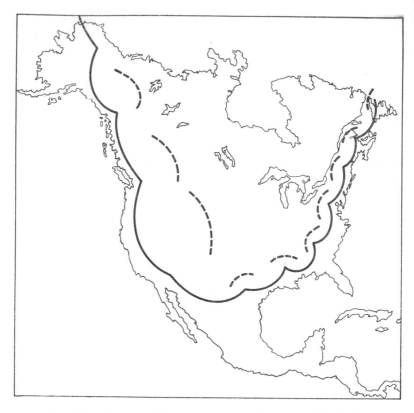

2.12. The Appalachian mountain system as it may have appeared in Pre-Cretaceous times (after Tuzo Wilson).

in the Appalachian complex – in Newfoundland, in the Gaspé Peninsula, in Quebec Province; in Pennsylvania, Tennessee, Oklahoma and Texas: *and all thrusting inland with their concave aspect towards the coast.* Thus with the analogy of the Rocky Mountains in their relation to the Sierra Nevada and the Coastal Mountains of British Columbia as guide, the geologists searched seawards from the junctions between the salients, presumed to be *secondary* arcs, for the faults which would lead them to the junctions of the *primary* arc system, should such exist. Five of these fault lines have in fact been identified, two in the north and three in the south; and traces of a sixth have been detected in the New York area, buried beneath a subsequent deposit of sedimentary rocks.

Next comes the search for remnants of the primary arcs which should lie between consecutive pairs of seaward-trending fault lines: and sure enough, the appropriate volcanic rocks are found cropping out across Newfoundland, Nova Scotia, New Brunswick, New England, and inland from the coastal plain which lies north of Florida and the Gulf of Mexico. Moreover, traces of the sedimentary rocks of the outer member of a double mountain arc system have been identified in Newfoundland and Nova Scotia in the north, and in Virginia and the Carolinas in the south.

All these rocks, volcanic and sedimentary alike, date from the Carboniferous period; and the evidence is therefore reasonably complete that the Appalachians were at that time a seven-fold system of active mountain arcs. But here comes a new conundrum: for the threefold system of mountain arcs, active at the present day, which lie on the western seaboard of the North American continent – namely, the British Columbian, United States, and Mexican arcs – dates from the same Carboniferous period as the Appalachians. It looks indeed as if the whole North American continent had in the Carboniferous period been girdled with a complete ring of mountain arcs, ten in number, and that in post-Carboniferous times the main fracture zone of the earth's crust had switched its direction through a complete right angle: that instead of swinging east from the Mexican arc into the Appalachian system, it thrust south to the Andes, leaving the Appalachians to die of an early old age. We shall return to this most interesting and subtle question in Chapter 5.

THE OLDEST FORMATIONS

North of the Appalachians are the remnants of two mountain ranges whose rocks are the oldest in the world: namely the Laurentian shield, and that of the Keewatin province, lying respectively east and south of Hudson Bay in Canada, the one 1,000 million years old, the other aged 2,500 million years.

Yet even here faint traces of arcuate structure can be found imprinted on the surface rocks; although erosion, subsequent uplift to re-establish isostatic equilibrium, further erosion, and moreover massive glaciation, have obliterated all but the deepest basins of the original arcs. And there is a striking

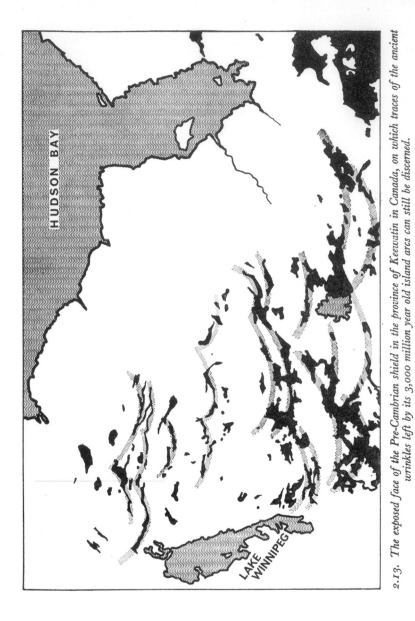

2.13. *The exposed face of the Pre-Cambrian shield in the province of Keewatin in Canada, on which traces of the ancient wrinkles left by its 3,000 million year old island arcs can still be discerned.*

difference between them: the lavas of the Laurentian system are andesitic, the pillow lavas of the Keewatin province are basaltic, like the isolated volcanic islands of the Pacific.

Thus it would appear that the basaltic rocks of Keewatin

were formed by volcanic action through the primitive crust of the earth, the five-kilometre basaltic layer which as we have already seen forms at once the ocean floor and the basement of the continents. Subsequently, around two thousand million years ago, the character of the continental rocks changed from highly basic to preponderantly acidic – examples of this transition being found for instance in the Finno-Scandinavian shield, aged one thousand eight hundred million years.

CONTINENTAL GROWTH

Having traced the formation of the world's mountain systems back from the youngest island arcs of the Pacific to the ancient continental nuclei, it remains to make a survey in the opposite direction in time, namely from the oldest to the youngest: and immediately the idea of an *evolutionary growth* of the continents springs to the mind (see Plate VIII). Thus two thousand five hundred million years ago came the first volcanoes, closely parallel lines of basaltic peaks marking the first conical fractures of the upper mantle and crust; two thousand million years ago came the change in the character of the lavas belched out through the cracks in the crust, from basaltic to andesitic, marking the first stage of continental growth – the accumulation of the metamorphosed sediments originating from aerial erosion of the first andesitic volcanic peaks, of which the shields of eastern Canada and of Scandinavia are the scarred remnants; a thousand million years ago saw the birth of yet another continental zone; and from two hundred to five hundred million years ago occurred the formation of the mountain arcs seaward of the older formations which can be clearly recognised as such today.

This idea of a zonal growth of a continent outwards from a first primitive nucleus, each zone younger than the last, is in keeping with the remarkable results of the recent surveys of data on the radio-active dating of igneous and metamorphic rocks, such as accumulate during the formation of active mountain arcs. These surveys indicate that mountain building has occurred in the past in quite well-defined spurts: for the ages of the rocks examined are sharply grouped around the dates 200 million, 1,000 million, 1,800 million and 2,600 million years ago.

A final loose end needs to be tied up in this story of mountain building from the substance of the mantle: namely to demonstrate that the rate of emission of lava from all the volcanoes of the world over a period of 3,000 million years is sufficient to account for the total bulk of all the continents, which amounts to some six thousand million cubic kilometres.

Now five hundred volcanoes in all are known to have been active in historical times, with an estimated total emission of 320 cubic kilometres of lava since A.D. 1500. This is equivalent to an average rate of emission of just on one cubic kilometre per annum. Allowing then for the higher than average volcanism evidenced by the older rocks, a total emission since the first Pre-Cambrian eruptions of the required six thousand million cubic kilometres of lava is not unreasonable.

So an answer can now be given to the question posed earlier at p. 47: How shall we interpret the first chapter of geological history, the formation of the gigantic mountains of which the continental shields are the seventh age? The answer is quite simply that all the mountains in the world, all the great continental rafts of the earth's crust, have been launched from the upper mantle along the slipways of conical fracture, in at least four distinct outbursts of volcanic action, marking as many stages in the zonal growth of the continents from the first basaltic nuclei of two thousand five hundred million years ago.

CHAPTER 3

The Ocean Floor

I F the oceans could be drained of their five million million cubic feet of water, what would a spying satellite see as it circumnavigated the globe?

It would see the floor of the Arctic Ocean divided into three deep basins, ten thousand feet or more below continental level. It would see the coastal mountains of Greenland as a sort of pie-crust around the deep hollow in the earth's surface sculpted by the weight of the ice cap. It would see a gigantic range of mountains running plumb down the middle of the Atlantic, torn throughout its length of 10,000 miles by a great rift valley, six thousand feet deep and thirty miles wide. It would see the highest cliffs in the world, a sheer plunge of twenty thousand feet, north of the Falkland Islands. Antarctica would come into view as part continent, part archipelago. The Atlantic Ridge would be seen swinging round the Cape of Good Hope into the West Indian Ocean. Our satellite would see the Pacific Ocean girdled on the west with a string of ocean arcs and chasmic trenches; the floor of the ocean studded with hundreds of volcanic sea-mounts; to the east the great hump of the East Pacific Rise. It would see the great faults in the sea bed off the western coast of North America, swinging away from the San Andreas fault on land.

This detailed knowledge of the bottom of the sea has been won during the past forty years from the increasingly systematic use of a single observational method – that of *echo-sounding*.

The echo-sounder is a sword which has been beaten into a ploughshare – or maybe in this case into Neptune's trident: for it began away back in World War I, the brainchild of Pierre Langevin of France and Ernest Rutherford of England, as a weapon against the German U-boats.

Langevin and Rutherford's line of reasoning was this:

"We've all had our fun in listening to the echo of a shout sent back from cliff or corrie; and we've all recognised the fact that the further away the reflecting surface the longer we have to wait for the echo. Send out a short pulse of supersonic vibration from a destroyer or 'Q-ship', and if you get an echo back it's a U-boat."

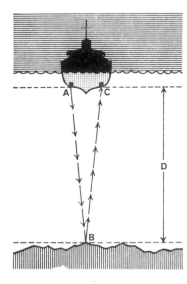

3.1. A simple form of echo-sounder, still in use by (e.g.) trawl fishermen in their search for herring shoals, or to guide them on their way as they traverse the shallows above the banks. . . . The 'ping' sent out from the supersonic transmitter A is reflected by the sea-bed at B; the 'pong' of the echo is reported by the receiver C. The time which has elapsed between 'ping' and 'pong' tells the navigator the depth D of the sea bed below the keel of his boat.

And now for Neptune's trident, first used to good purpose in 1925 by the German oceanographic vessel *Meteor* in her exploration of the Atlantic sea-bed. The idea is this: Built into the keel of the ship are a supersonic transmitter, as also a supersonic receiver tuned to the same frequency. The transmitter and receiver alike may be essentially short cylinders of a special magnetic alloy, which has the property of contracting spasmically when given a magnetic shock from a sudden surge of current in the coil surrounding it. Thus the transmitting cylinder goes 'ping'. The identical receiver 'listens' for the 'pong' echoing back from the sea bottom, 'hears' it, contracts, and sends an induced electric current through its coil to the receiving stylus, which has already marked the instant of the 'ping' on a revolving drum. Knowing the velocity of sound in sea-water, the time interval which has elapsed between signal and response gives you the depth below surface of the sea bottom.

From these primitive beginnings has grown up a whole new technology of echo-sounding. Tens of thousands of miles of

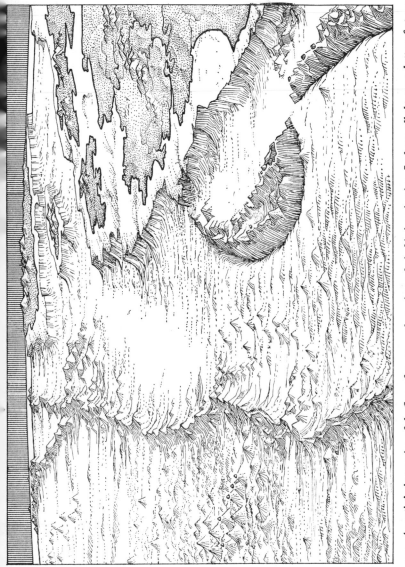

3.2. *An artist's impression of the floor of an ocean that exists only in his imagination. It shows all the ocean bottom features in a single picture: the continental land mass, the continental shelf, the continental slope, the abyssal plains, a mid-ocean ridge and the volcanic islands and the island arcs and trenches characteristic of the Pacific.*

underwater profiles lying beneath the tracks of ocean-going vessels have been logged. The relative accuracy of the depths recorded has steadily increased until, with a sophisticated modern apparatus such as you see in Plate X, the ups and downs in the ocean floor below the ship's track can be read off with an accuracy of 1 in 3,000. Note however that here 'accuracy' means 'relative accuracy': for the *absolute* accuracy depends on the value taken for the velocity of sound in an idealised 'sea-water', water which can in practice vary in density, salinity, and temperature from one location to another over the enormous expanse of the world ocean, within considerably wider limits than 1 in 3,000.

Thus the *bathymetric charts* – maps of the ocean floor, in other words, such as that of Plate XI – which are constructed from the logs of the ships' tracks, are accurate in *absolute* depth to not more than say 1 in 500. Nevertheless, here is a navigational aid of the future. Already ocean-going submarines like the *Nautilus* can find their way around from the very special information supplied to them by their governments about the topography of the ocean floor; and the day may not be so far distant when *all* ocean-going vessels are free to navigate the high seas by echo-sounding rather than by the stars. And indeed already the trawler skippers out of little fishing ports in the county of Caithness in northern Scotland are using their echo-sounders as much to find their way home in fog as to search for the 'silver darlings'.

But what of the seascape revealed by the magic box of the echo-sounder? Already we have seen that it is no flat featureless plain such as was predicated in the old school-books. Instead, the modern oceanographer recognises at least six phases of ocean-bottom topography – the continental shelf, the continental slope, the abyssal plains; the mid-ocean ridges, the submerged sea-mounts of the Pacific, those deep ocean trenches which play such a big part in mountain building. Let's survey them, one by one.

CONTINENTAL SHELVES

Every continental land mass on the globe thrusts itself into at least one of its surrounding oceans as a submerged *continental shelf* – a gradually sloping platform of shallow seas, with a

Our earthbound astronomical observatories cannot take pictures of our own spiral
nebula, the Milky Way, for the simple reason that the solar system is a part of it. So here
is the next-best thing – a stunning photograph of M81 in Ursa Major, 10 million light
years distant from the Mount Palomar Observatory, where this picture was taken with
the 200-inch Hale telescope. The bright stars in this photograph, three of them visible
against the background of the nebula itself, are all in the Milky Way.

Plate I

On the island of Java: Mount Raung in volcanic eruption.

A PANORAMIC VIEW OF THE PRODUCTS OF THE MANTLE (PLATES II AND III)

Plate II

Mountain peaks in Kashmir on the east-west arm of the world-wide crustal zone of compression (see Chapter 2).

In the Fiji Islands of the Pacific.
In the foreground, the small island
and village of Qoma off the east
coast of Viti Levu: in the background
the island of Ovalau, its chief town
Levuka, once the capital of Fiji.

A near-vertical cliff of basalt rock
on the eastern flank of the Mid-
Atlantic Ridge, sunk 1,580
fathoms beneath the waves.

Plate III

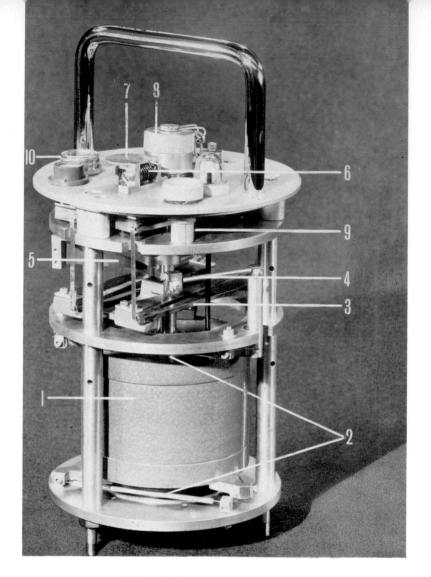

PORTRAIT OF A MODERN SEISMOMETER.

The instrument proper with its protective casing removed

An earth tremor passing through crust or upper mantle beneath the position of the seismometer on the earth's surface causes a heavy spring-mounted permanent magnet (1) to rise and fall on the crests and in the troughs of the seismic wave radiating from the focus of some near or distant earthquake. The magnet is constrained to move only in the direction of the axis of the whole instrument by a group of five positioning rods (2), one of which you can clearly see in the picture; and its natural period of oscillation can be adjusted to match the mean period of near or distant quakes by altering the tension of the supporting leaf-springs (3).

This adjustment is effected by controlling the pressure put on the spoke (4) by the leaf-spring (5) (see also detail in Plate V). The control is exerted by a worm and gear-wheel (6) and (7), mounted on the top plate of the instrument. The magnet can be clamped in transit by means of a clamping screw (8).

An important practical feature of the 'Willmore seismometer' is that it is fully tropicalised: thus the coil is 'potted' in epoxy resin; the leaf-springs supporting the magnet are made of a special material having a constant modulus of elasticity over the temperature range —40°C to +50°C; and a silica-gel desiccator (9) is built-in to the instrument.

Plate IV

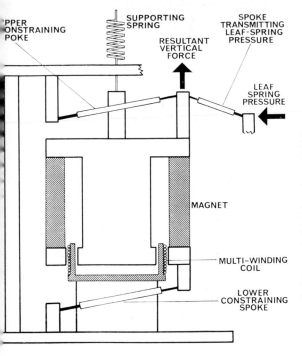

UPPER CONSTRAINING POKE

SUPPORTING SPRING

SPOKE TRANSMITTING LEAF-SPRING PRESSURE

RESULTANT VERTICAL FORCE

LEAF SPRING PRESSURE

MAGNET

MULTI–WINDING COIL

LOWER CONSTRAINING SPOKE

DETAIL OF THE MECHAN-ISM FOR ADJUSTING THE PERIOD OF OSCILLATION OF THE MAGNET.

The diagram also shows the multi-wound coil, fixed permanently in position between the poles of the magnet, in which an oscillating electric current is induced by the quaking magnet. This current is led via a six-pin waterproof connector, shown at (10) in Plate IV, to a transistor amplifier, and thence to the pen which traces out the seismogram.

A seismogram showing the arrival of the direct seismic wave at Pg, which has travelled through the surface rocks of the earth's crust, ahead of that at Pn of the wave which has been refracted at the moho. . . . This record was taken with the Willmore Seismometer illustrated in Plate IV, 'listening' near Newton Stewart in Wigtownshire in Scotland for the arrival of waves sent out from the explosion of 50 kilograms of high explosive, deto-nated in 180 feet of water below the surface of Loch Striven, 113 kilometres to the west.

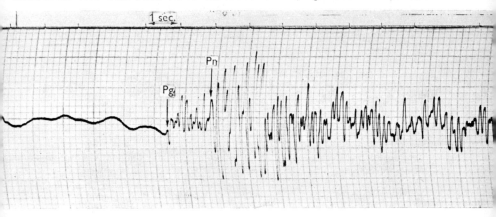

1 sec.

Pn

Pg

Plate V

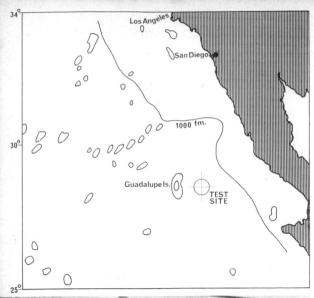

The island of Guadalupe
(after W. Bascom)

BORING A HOLE IN
THE ISLAN

Conical guide for the
drill pipe

CUSS I

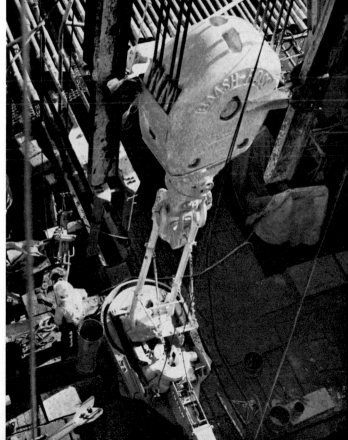

Raising a length of drill
pipe

Pillow lavas in the Keewatin province of Canada, south of Hudson Bay, formed 2,800 million years ago.

The North Cape of Norway, on the edge of the Finno-Scandinavian shield, aged 2,000 million years.

Plate VIII

LANDSCAPES ILLUSTRATING THREE PHASES OF CONTINENTAL GROWTH

Darjeeling, in the 1,000 million-year-old hill country of Assam.

width varying from a few miles off Monaco in the Mediterranean, or off the Island of Bermuda in the western Atlantic, to a hundred miles or more off the Arctic border of northern Asia.

Now you may still read in school textbooks of 'Physical Geography' that the shallow seas are the product of aeons of wave action on the margins of the continents: in other words, that the continental shelves are the result of *sea erosion*. In such books the inner stretches of the shelves are erroneously classified as *wave-cut terraces*, supposed to be carved out of the continental shores by the erosion of the ocean breakers. The outer margins of the shelves are pictured as *wave-built terraces*, deposits of silt and sediment cast up by the waves or deposited by rivers. The margin of the shelves is referred to in such books as *the wave base*, because seawards of the shelf all wave action is assumed to have ceased.

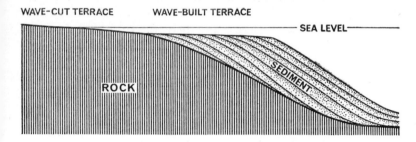

WAVE-CUT TERRACE   WAVE-BUILT TERRACE

SEA LEVEL

ROCK

SEDIMENT

3.3. The false picture of the origin of the continental shelves, as being the work of the sea waves rather than that of aerial and glacial erosion: still propagated in some of the less advanced schools and colleges (after Shephard).

This tired old stuff has in the past few decades been ruthlessly scrapped by the modern echo-sounder, the under-water camera, the oil drill and the aqualung diver: and four chief reasons can now be advanced against the idea of a wave-born continental shelf.

First, the echo-sounder has revealed that the substratum of the shelf, right out to the edge of the continental slope, is solid rock, even where it is covered by sediments deposited off the mouths of the great rivers. Second, these same sediments are so variable in grain size, indeed almost capriciously so, that they couldn't possibly have been laid down by the ocean waves,

65

E

which deposit their coarser burden first, their finer-grained cargo nearer in-shore. Third, the depth of the outer margins of the shelf bears no relation whatsoever to the prevailing size of the waves beating upon them. And fourth, the topography of the shelf is at times that of hill country on land, as is beautifully illustrated in Plate XII.

The complex picture of the continental shelves of the world delineated by modern methods is in marked contrast to the simple old sketch of the standardised wave-cut terrace. In the first place, there is the sharp difference in the width of the shelf in the Atlantic and Pacific basins. On the whole, the shelf off the continental margins of the Pacific is much narrower than those of the Atlantic, or may even be lacking altogether: for the Pacific Ocean is bordered chiefly by young mountain arcs and trenches which do not yet allow of the formation of large river systems, depositing the products of erosion on the sea-bed; in any case not in the time available since their birth. In the Atlantic, it is true that narrow shelves occur off the coast of Florida and Cape Hatteras: but here the absence of a wide shelf is due to the scouring action of the Gulf Stream, sweeping northwards at the rate of three or four miles an hour.

Wide continental shelves occur all over the world seaward of the mouths of large rivers: off the northern coast of Siberia, off the mouth of the Amazon, in the Persian Gulf, in the Bay of Bengal. In seas with the right temperature and salinity, as off the coast of Queensland in Australia, coral growth can lead to an exceptionally wide shelf.

GLACIATION OF THE SHELF

On both sides of the North Atlantic, the continental shelves appear to have been carved mainly by the action of glaciers. Twenty thousand years ago the Arctic Ocean was in all probability an open sea, hence the last Pleistocene ice age: a sufficiently paradoxical statement until you hear the interpretation of Maurice Ewing of the Lamont Institute in New York State.

The argument runs thus: an ice-free Arctic Ocean would entail a winter temperature only 3.5° centigrade higher than at present, but with a corresponding increase in vapour pressure by a factor of not less than 50; while the summer temperature and vapour pressure would show only a small increase above

66

the winter values. Hence throughout the year there would be heavy snowfalls in the northern hemisphere, packing to glacial ice over the land and around the coasts. An ever increasing amount of water would be taken from the sea and deposited on land, until finally all communication between the Atlantic and Arctic Oceans over the Arctic sill would be cut off. Thereafter, the Arctic Ocean would freeze, precipitation would decrease, the glaciers would retreat, sea-level would rise, until once again warm Atlantic water would have free access to the Arctic basin: and the cycle would repeat itself. At the present time, we are fast approaching another phase of ice-free waters around the pole – and a repetition within the next 10,000 years of the Pleistocene ice-age.

At the height of the Pleistocene ice-age, sea-level would have been not less than 100 metres below its present value. Thus the whole of the Atlantic continental shelf would have been exposed to ice action. Evidence of such action is indeed to be found to this day: in glacial debris off the Norwegian coast, in the fishing banks of Newfoundland and the North Sea, in the numerous shallow basins which are equivalent to the lakes gouged out by glacial action on land – and, often hidden by the subsequent deposit of sediments, genuine wave-cut terraces at the margin of the shelf.

Summing up: the continental shelves have been formed, not by sea erosion, but *by deposition* – either by rivers, or by coral growth; and eroded by the winds and by glacial action at a period of low sea-level. Narrow shelves are found either seaward of young mountain arcs, or where fast currents move parallel to the shore.

CONTINENTAL SLOPES

The continental shelf ends abruptly, at an average depth of 300 feet, in a steep slope. The gentle gradient of the shelf, of perhaps 1 in 500, up which it would be quite easy to ride a bike, increases within a mile or so to perhaps 1 in 4, which would tax a tank.

The *continental slopes* mark the true boundaries of the land masses, and they do so in no uncertain fashion in their plunge to the true ocean depths. Thus for example the foot of the escarpment off the west coast of South America is 42,000 feet

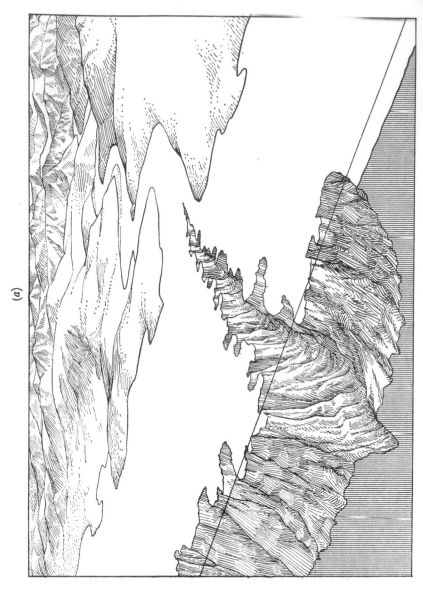

3.4(a), (b). Two examples of submarine canyons: the one an integral part of the topography of a river estuary, the other

below the tops of the Andes, that is almost twice the height of
the southern aspect of the Himalayas; while a drop of 10,000
feet is quite commonly to be found. Usually the slope is con-
tinous between the margin of the continental shelf and the deep

(b)

sea floor; occasionally, however, you find an intermediate terrace, as for example off the coast of Florida, or even a series of basins and hills, as off the coast of California.

A feature common to almost all continental slopes is the

presence of *deep-sea canyons*, steep-sided gashes in the slope that at times rival the Grand Canyon on land in both length and depth. Sometimes these submerged canyons are quite clearly the continuation of the continental river valleys, like the Hudson Canyon off New York or the Congo Canyon off the west coast of Africa. But far more often they bear no relation whatsoever to the adjacent continental river topography.

The origin of these awe-inspiring submarine canyons, first observed at the beginning of the present century, was hotly debated for upwards of fifty years. The preferred hypothesis over this period was that they arose from glacial action in Pleistocene times, although Kuenen of Groningen in Holland had demonstrated by laboratory models that they could be reproduced in all their characteristic features by turbidity currents – turbulent streams of water carrying solids in suspension.

The matter was clinched in favour of Kuenen's turbidity currents in 1952, when Bruce Heezen and Maurice Ewing of Columbia, New York, published their celebrated 'Who-dun-it' on the destruction of the submarine cables off the Grand Banks of Newfoundland on November 18 1929.

To quote from Jacobs, Russell and Wilson's *Physics and Geology*:

"On November 18, 1929, at 2032 G.M.T., a severe earthquake of magnitude 7·2 shook the continental shelf and continental slope south of Newfoundland. The epicenter lay beneath the continental slope where it is at a depth of between 2000 and 4000 m in a region crossed by many transAtlantic cables. The six cables closest to the epicenter were broken immediately, but cables at successively greater distances in increasingly deeper water for 500 km south of the epicenter were in turn broken during the following 13 hr, 17 min after the quake. On the other hand, none of those lying nearby to the north on the continental shelf were disturbed. Repair ships found that sections of the broken cables were removed or buried over an area which was 600 km long and narrow in the north but 500 km broad in the south. Half of the breaks occurred on the ocean floor at the foot of the continental slopes in places where the gradient is less than 1°.

3.5. The Newfoundland Grand Banks turbidity current of November 18 1929, triggered by an earthquake on the edge of the continental shelf, which fractured successively six and then three cables (in all nine) as it tore its way down the continental shelf (after Heezen and Ewing).

"Heezen and Ewing showed that the above observations could be explained as the result of a great flow of muddy water – in fact a turbidity current – initiated by mud slumping near the epicenter and subsequently being diluted by mixing with water. The intervals between interruptions of messages in different cables showed that the current had reached a velocity of over 100 km/hr on the continental slopes and that it had progressively lost speed. Cores taken later showed that a graded bed averaging 1 m in thickness had been deposited over an area of 200,000 km^2 and that the flow had traveled for over 1000 km from the epicenter."

Since the date of Heezen and Ewing's important discovery, upwards of thirty contemporary turbidity currents, ripping down their submarine canyons with a freight of stones and silt from the continental shelf, have been recognised: which finally makes nonsense of the glacial-action theories. Moreover, the recording of these turbidity currents has shown that their erosive action in the great sunken canyons is *sporadic* – quite like that of the water which progressively gouges out the wadis of the Indian desert during each season of the monsoon rains (see Plate XIII).

THE ABYSSAL PLAINS

Next, the *abyssal plains*, discovered as late as 1947 by the *Atlantis* out of Woods Hole, New England: stretches of featureless sediment which even the eye of the under-water camera of Plate XIV sees as completely smooth. Actually, they are misnamed. They are not completely flat. They tail into the continental slope quite regularly and continuously, with a gradient that begins seaward at say 1 in 2,000, to finish with perhaps 1 in 500 at the foot of the slope in the so-called 'continental rise'. They are most probably formed from the detritus torn from the continental shelf by turbidity currents which, laden with rocks and sediment, come roaring over the edge of the shelf to deposit their load at the foot of the slope, coarser material first, the finest-grained silt last: obliterating completely the rough topography of the true ocean floor.

There is indeed a marked contrast between the sediments recovered by modern coring devices from the surface of the

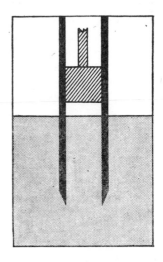

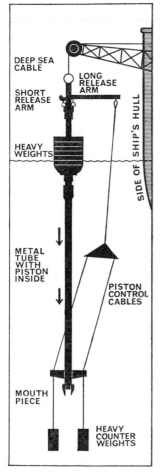

3.6.(a), (b). *The piston corer in the primitive form so successfully exploited by its inventor, Bjorge Kullenberg of Gothenburg in Sweden. The principle on which the Kullenberg corer and its more elaborate successors works is clearly shown in Fig. 3.6(a). The corer, weighted for penetration into the ocean sediments, is lowered over the side of the mother ship counterpoised by two heavy weights which dangle below it as it descends through the superjacent water. The counterweights strike bottom first, thereby tripping the long/short-arm lever above. The weighted core tube plummets vertically to the ocean bottom, and penetrates the surface of the sediments. The piston which you see in Fig. 3.6(b) now comes into operation: it abhors the vacuum which the continued descent of its cylinder tends to create between the bottom of the piston and the surface of the sediments, and hence drives the cylinder over deeper, until a core of up to 70 feet in length is forced up inside it – to be recovered by winding the whole apparatus back above the waves by means of the stout engine-driven winch on deck (after Kullenberg and Hans Pettersen).*

abyssal plains and those from the adjacent continental rise. The former consist essentially of shallow water quartz sands, grey clays and silts, such as would be carried seawards by turbidity currents originating at the edge of the continental shelf; the latter almost entirely of the calcareous skeletons of the so-called zooplankton of the surface waters of the ocean –

delicate little foraminifera whose exquisitely formed bones drift down through hundreds of fathoms of sea-water to rest in the ooze covering the continental rise and the lower slopes of the mid-ocean mountains.

The thickness of the deep ocean sediments in both the Atlantic and Pacific Oceans has been measured in scores of places by seismic methods, the average thickness being about 2,000 feet in the Atlantic and 1,000 feet in the Pacific. These figures are wildly at variance with estimates based on the amount of silt carried oceanwards by all the rivers of the world over the whole of geological time, which give an average thickness for the deep sea sediments of approximately *two miles*. We shall return to this discrepancy in the next chapter.

MID-OCEAN MOUNTAINS

Plumb down the middle of the Atlantic Ocean runs a majestic range of submerged mountains – the Mid-Atlantic Ridge. No mountain range on land can compare with it, not only in size, but in the stark outline of its peaks and rocky terraces, that may lie a mile or more beneath the Atlantic waves. No winds have smoothed and rounded its slopes since they were first formed, no rivers carry fragments year by year from the heights to fill and soften the bottom valleys. It is a silent world, unbroken even by the descent of myriads of radiolarians falling softly like snow from the surface waters above.

With the exception of a handful of its highest peaks, which thrust themselves above the waves in the Azores, in the Peak of Teneriffe, in Ascension Island, in Tristan da Cunha, the contours of the Mid-Atlantic Ridge can be traced only by the listening ear of the echo-sounder. The first rough outlines of the ridge were mapped as early as 1925 by the echo-sounders of the German research vessel *Meteor*; but it was not until 1953 that the full majesty and importance of the Mid-Atlantic Mountains were recognised, following the analysis of numerous traverses of the ridge by *Vema*, the oceanographic research vessel of Lamont Geological Observatory, New York.

This analysis, when displayed as a detailed physiographic map of the floor of the Atlantic, revealed a deep rift valley splitting the crest of the Mid-Atlantic Ridge throughout its long length from Greenland in the north to Tristan da Cunha in the south.

74

3.7. A section of the Mid-Atlantic Ridge, showing the median rift valley which splits it along its entire length (after Heezen).

It was immediately recognised at Lamont that the newly discovered rift in the Mid-Atlantic Ridge coincided exactly with the belt of shallow earthquakes which was already known to extend from north to south beneath the floor of the Atlantic Ocean. That was in 1953. But by the mid-50's seismographs had traced a 40,000-mile belt of mid-ocean earthquake epicentres along the bottom of the Arctic Ocean, of the North and South Atlantic, of the Indian Ocean off the east coast of

3.8. The chain of shallow earthquakes which marks the path of the Mid-Atlantic rift valley (after Heezen).

Africa, as well as in the South Pacific. This led Maurice Ewing and Bruce Heezen in 1956 to predict that the rifted ridge of the Mid-Atlantic was only one section of a world-wide rift in the ocean bottom, contiguous with the earthquake belt.

During the IGY, research vessels engaged in the oceanographic programme observed isolated profiles of the mid-ocean rift valley in many parts of the world; and in early 1960 the Lamont oceanographic vessel *Vema* made a cruise in the Indian Ocean specifically to look for it – and found it, stretching unbroken from Marion Island in the south to Rodriguez Island off Mauritius in the north. And, in the spring of 1962, the British hydrographic vessel H.M.S. *Owen*, with Loncarevic and Matthews of the Cambridge Geophysical Laboratory on board, brought home the news that the Indian Ocean rift valley extends still further north, right down the middle of the Carlsberg Ridge in the Arabian Sea, first discovered by the echo-sounder of the Danish vessel *Dana* in 1920–22.

Clearly we are faced here with a major feature of the topography of the earth's crust, quite as important to our understanding of crustal evolution as the mountain systems we surveyed in the last chapter. The rift valley which splits the great mid-ocean ridge throughout its length is no mere scratch in the ocean floor: the profiles mapped by the echo-sounder show a steep-sided valley thousands of miles long, 6,000 feet deep, 30 miles wide; as compared with 60 miles, 4,000 feet, 10 miles for the Grand Canyon. Moreover, its physical characteristics are unique: the ocean floor below the mid-ocean ridges is hot; gravity measurements indicate a thinning of the crust in their neighbourhood; seismic observations yield a characteristic velocity below the rift valley of 7·8 km/sec, characteristic of the mantle rather than the basalt floor of the oceans. Finally, there is evidence that the whole mid-ocean ridge system is geologically young – basaltic rock dredged from the Mid-Atlantic Ridge, dated by the potassium-argon method, is a mere 10 million years old.

Now the mid-ocean rift valley comes ashore in at least two places – in the graben of Iceland and in the Great Rift Valley of East Africa which you can see in Plate XV. Both these

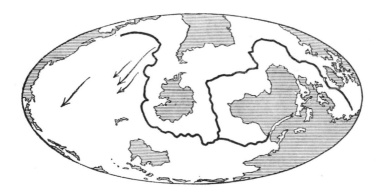

3.9. The world-wide zone of tension in the earth's crust, scribed on the ocean floor by the rift valley atop the mid-ocean ridges. West of the East Pacific Rise, the three slender arrows at right angles to its western flank mark the strings of islands so characteristic of the Pacific – the Tuamoto Gambier, the Society, the Tuabuai Islands; the single arrow in mid-ocean traces the line of the Hawaiian Islands.

77

terrestrial features have long been recognised as splits in the earth's crust, torn asunder *under tension*; and the conclusion is forced upon us that the whole mid-ocean ridge system is a *zone of tension* in the earth's crust, of comparable importance on a world scale with the mountain arc *zone of compression* dealt with in the preceding chapter.

ISLANDS IN THE PACIFIC

The topography of the Pacific Ocean is in many ways in a class apart. Already in Chapter 2 the island arcs and trenches shoreward of the 'andesite line' have been discussed. Seaward of the andesite line lie the isolated volcanic islands, the coral atolls, and the submerged flat-topped sea-mounts which are our business in this chapter.

Tom Gaskell of the British Petroleum Company writes in his imaginative book *Under the Deep Oceans*:

"If only the sea could be drained away, the view from the great peak of Mauna Loa in Hawaii would out-rival any Japanese print of beautiful symmetrical volcanic peaks. Rising with graceful curves from a vast flat ocean-floor, the smooth slopes of the mountains would be unspoilt by the eroding action of glaciers and rivers. Some of the peaks would be like crowns, their tops encircled by a regular rim of coral rock, and most of these would be at exactly the same height, for they are the atolls which rise only a few feet above sea-level. There would be many other flat-topped peaks of lesser height, looking as if some fickle giant had arbitrarily lopped off the peaks of volcanoes to provide seats and tables. Interspersed with these would be regular cones of all sizes and ages, some smoking as a sign that nature's builders are still at work. For many years these lovely volcanic features of the Pacific have aroused speculation, especially the truncated cones which are unfamiliar on land, but the combination of seismic and echo-sounder measurements has succeeded in unravelling this mystery, so that now a single mechanism can explain them all."

In the formation of a typical volcanic island of the Pacific we are most probably witnessing a repetition of the birth of the basaltic continental nuclei from the substance of the primeval

78

crust. At first lava from the mantle wells up through cracks in the five-mile thick ocean floor like oil from a gusher, a freely flowing viscous liquid, which is quickly cooled by the surrounding water to form great heaps of porous clinker on the ocean floor. Once above the waves, however, the character of the melt alters: it solidifies in the air to form a hermetically sealed solid cap, entrapping pools of molten lava whose volume can be as much as several cubic kilometres. Then you have a volcanic island, whose cratered mountain peaks erupt violently between quiescent periods.

Now coral atolls and submerged sea-mounts alike were once just such volcanic peaks rising out of the waters of the Pacific. Then, either because the whole ocean basin began to sink, or perhaps in some cases because the ocean floor beneath individual islands buckled under their weight, these volcanic peaks began to subside beneath the waves. Those rimmed by upward-growing coral reefs remain to this day with their heads above water as atolls: the vast majority – around nineteen out of twenty – sank below sea-level to become flat-topped sea-mounts.

Coral reefs are built by the coral colyp – a fleshy, delicate little animal form, whose portrait you see in Plate XVI – and a humble little seaweed called *Zooxanthella corallinacea*, working together in symbiotic partnership.

The coral polyp itself is very sensitive to its environment: it can function only in clear sea water whose temperature lies between 68° and 90° Fahrenheit, with a salinity of between 27 and 40 parts per thousand. It is little else in form but a tiny flexible bottle with a hungry mouth of predatory tentacles, ready to snatch any bits and pieces of zooplankton which come drifting past on the ocean swell: so fragile that it can live only if protected by the delicate calcareous skeleton that we know familiarly as 'coral'.

The external skeleton of the coral polyp is however too fragile to build a coral reef: and it is here that Zooxanthella takes over. This little one-celled alga feeds on the waste products of the polyp, and in exchange supplies the coral with an ample amount of carbonate with which to build a stout sea-wall against the ocean breakers.

Thus where a sinking volcanic cone was surrounded at contemporary sea-level with a coral reef, coral polyp and its

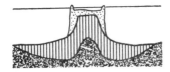

3.10. Illustrating successive stages in the birth of a coral atoll.

companion alga could build upward fast enough to beat the rate of subsidence of their island. The sinking top of the peak would at one stage get lopped off by the ocean breakers, which would also scour out the familiar lagoon inland from the protecting reef.

This picture of the formation of coral atolls, first advocated by Charles Darwin during the classic voyage of the *Beagle* in 1835, was for years the subject of heated debate; but a combination of modern seismic prospecting and deep drilling have in the last decade established beyond dispute that the coral crown of a Pacific atoll does indeed rest below sea level on basaltic volcanic rock.

The flat-topped sea-mounts which stud the floor of the Pacific are now seen to be either atolls that didn't make the grade, or else sunken volcanic peaks once upthrust in waters which were unsuitable for the coral polyp. Their flat tops mark the stage in their subsidence when they were just awash: when the pounding of the Pacific surf would shear off their friable laval tops to give the truncated cones which the modern echo-sounder records in their hundreds.

And here comes a very remarkable fact: that no lavas; no fossils, either in the islands or on the surrounding sea-bed; no sediments in the Pacific, are older than the 250-million-year-old Cretaceous period. Now this same period saw the latest stage of mountain building, in the formation of the island arcs of the China seas; it saw the completion of the switch in the earth's zone of compressive fracture on the western margin of North America, from the Appalachians in the east to the Andes in the south; and in all probability it saw the birth of the Mid-Atlantic Ridge.

Thus the comparatively recent intense volcanic activity in the Pacific basin, when viewed in a world-wide perspective, is seen as only one aspect of great changes in the surface features of the earth, during which the continents took their present stations on the globe and the oceans their present pattern. In the next chapter we shall discover how these changes came about.

F

CHAPTER 4

Drifting Continents

The discovery during the last decade of a world-wide complex of mid-ocean ridges, when set beside the earlier recognition of a great T-shaped belt of linked mountain arcs bordering the continents, has given us a completely new picture of the earth's crust: a picture not of one, but of two mountain systems of global significance. Both systems are seismically active – we recall that the mid-ocean ridge system was traced largely with the help of its shallow earthquakes – both are therefore hinged to the earth's mantle. But whereas the active mountain arcs on land delineate a zone of crustal fracture under *compression*, the mid-ocean ridges are torn apart along their centre by a rift valley under *tension*. At the bottom of the deep trenches which border on the mountain arcs, the crust is sucked down into the substance of the mantle; whereas the substance of the mantle wells upwards into the bed of the mid-ocean rift valleys.

CONVECTION CURRENTS IN THE MANTLE

On the basis of these observations, there is now strong reason to postulate the existence of *convection currents* in the mantle, such as were advocated by Vening-Meinesz of Utrecht to account for the negative gravity anomalies which he had observed from his submarine in the region of the deep ocean trenches of the Pacific. The intrusion of the material of the upper mantle beneath the trenches, its extrusion below the mid-ocean rift valley, would then be plausibly explained as the outward and visible sign of an internal turnover of convection cells in the body of the mantle itself.

At first sight it may seem strange to speak of convection currents in the presumably solid substance of the mantle: but here there are two factors which must be borne in mind.

First, there is the time scale of geological processes, which is measured in millions of years. Thus a substance which behaves as a rigid solid in transmitting the rapid stresses – measured in minutes or seconds in their duration – involved in earthquake shocks, could well show plastic creep under quite small stresses acting over a sufficiently long period of time. Unfortunately, there is here no real possibility of an experimental test: as de Sitter of Leyden has so cogently put it: "No experimenter is willing to leave the measurement of the results of his experiment to his grandchildren, and even such a span of time would not be sufficient to get a good imitation of a geological process."

Second, there is the now well established presence of the 'Gutenberg channel' in the upper mantle, as a zone of permanently plastic or semi-plastic material which may well mark the shallowest reaches of a lubrication channel between the convection cells: which could then be thought of as turning over like solid rollers between narrow streams of convective material, creeping upward towards the mid-ocean ridges, downward from the ocean trenches.

CRITICAL THICKNESS OF THE MANTLE

However that may be, once the possibility of convection cells in the body of the mantle is granted, the question of their number immediately arises. Now we have already seen that in the lifetime of the earth the liquid inner core has in all probability grown at the expense of the mantle; and it is therefore pertinent to enquire whether the number of possible convection cells in the body of the mantle has remained constant as its thickness has diminished. This query has been answered by Runcorn of Newcastle-upon-Tyne, who has shown theoretically that the number of convection cells increases in a series of four distinct jumps: the first when the ratio of the radius of the liquid core r_c to that of the earth r_e takes the value 0·06; the second when $r_c/r_e=0·36$; the third when $r_c/r_e=0·49$; the fourth when $r_c/r_e=0·54$; the value at the present day, as deduced from the study of deep earthquakes, being 0·55.

CRITICAL DATES IN GEOLOGICAL HISTORY

We recall that our first pointer to the possible existence of convection currents in the mantle was the presence in the

83

crust of a world-wide zone of crustal compression, another of crustal tension, both marked by vigorous mountain building. One asks therefore whether abrupt changes in the convection pattern in the mantle, such as have been described in the last section, may not lead to major changes in the pattern of mountain building. In other words, can we *date* the jumps in the number of convection cells in the mantle by successive bursts of mountain building which, as we have already seen, the radio-active clocks have signalled as occurring 2,600, 1,800, 1,000, and 250 million years ago?

If then we plot the ratio r_c/r_e against time, and identify the jumps in the number of convection cells in the mantle with the radio-active age peaks, we get the curve for the rate of increase of the inner core at the expense of the mantle which is illustrated in Fig. 4.1 – and the next question is whether this curve corresponds to reality.

Now Runcorn has shown, on the simple assumption that the rate at which iron from the mantle is surrendered to the liquid core is proportional to the surface area of the core and to the mass of iron remaining in the core, that the radius of the core will at first increase linearly with time, and will then bend over

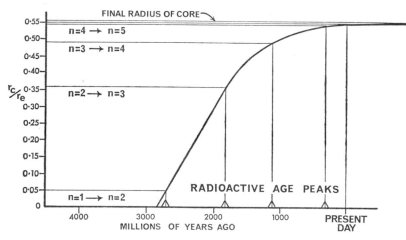

4.1. The pattern of convection cells in the substance of the mantle changes kaleido-scopically as the ratio $r_c : r_e$ of the radii of core and earth assumes a succession of four discrete values. Each such critical change can be identified with four successive bursts of mountain building in the crust, as revealed by age-peaks in the radio-active dating of the rocks (after Runcorn).

84

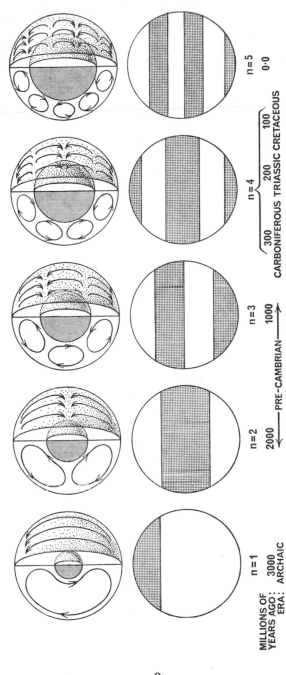

4.2. *The inner core of the earth grows at the expense of the mantle as the iron content of the mantle is surrendered to it (after Runcom).*

to approach its final value, which it reaches when no more iron is left in the mantle. In other words, he has been able to show quantitatively that the actual rate of growth of the earth's core is that predicted from the identification of the dates in the past at which the convection cells in the mantle increased in number with the radio-active age peaks in mountain building.

CRUSTAL PATTERNS OF LAND AND SEA

Reverting now to the beginning of the argument for convection currents in the mantle, namely the juxtaposition of a zone of intrusion along continental boundaries against a zone of extrusion in mid ocean, in a global pattern of crustal compression versus tension: one is faced with the conclusion that the whole crustal pattern of land and sea as it is today reflects the contemporary pattern of the convection cells in the mantle. Or put it this way: that the world's oceans lie above ascending currents, its continents above the descending currents in the mantle beneath them.

The question then arises whether the crustal pattern in the past corresponded to the appropriate convection pattern of the mantle as it was at any one epoch. If so, then 3,000 million years ago, in the dawn of the geological history of the earth, there may have been but a single land mass on the earth's surface; between 2,000 and 1,000 million years ago, in Pre-Cambrian times, there would have been two continental land masses; while between 300 and 100 million years ago, that is during the time between the Carboniferous and Cretaceous periods, the pattern in the crustal kaleidoscope switched from the dual land masses of the Cambrian era, possibly through certain intermediate stages, to the distribution of land and sea we observe today.

CONTINENTAL DRIFT

The conclusion of a purely geophysical argument, then, as epitomised in Fig. 4.2, is to assert the validity of the hypothesis of *continental drift*, advanced as far back as 1912 by Wegener and later by Du Toit: particularly in the form advocated by Du Toit, who postulated that fragmentation of two proto-continents, Laurasia in the northern hemisphere and Gondwanaland in the south, took place in the Mid-Mesozoic era.

86

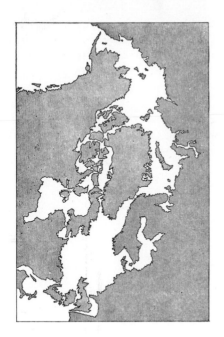

(a)

4.3. The proto-continents of the Cambrian era, (a) Laurasia and (b) Gondwanaland.

(b)

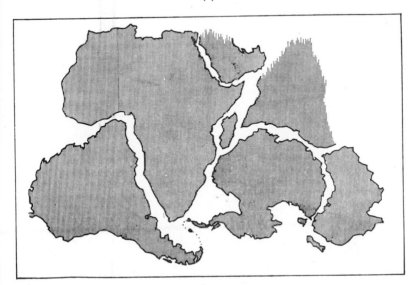

Wegener and Du Toit based their hypotheses on a host of geological criteria – physiographical, stratigraphical, paleoclimatic, paleontological: on largely qualitative similarities in the jig-saw fit of certain coast-lines, in the parallelism of geological strata found in the dispersed continental fragments; in the evidence for similar ancient climates in widely separated areas of the globe; in the occurrence of fossils of the same type in the component parts of paleozoic Gondwanaland.

Yet for the best part of fifty years geophysicists have tended to discount the evidence advanced by these pioneers, and that chiefly on two grounds: first, that no appropriate mechanism could be found for the sliding of large continental land masses over an ocean floor presumed to be rigid; and second, the apparent unlikelihood of the sudden occurrence of continental drift so late in geological history.

Both these objections, however, have now been met, following the discovery of the 40,000 mile-long zone of tension atop the mid-ocean ridges, on the one hand; and in the growing realisation that the Cretaceous period was a critical period in the history of the earth's crust, on the other. Continental drift must now be considered seriously as a major event – or better, series of events – in recorded geological time.

Thus reverting to the summary of events in the Cretaceous period – or rather more widely, in the Mesozoic era – listed at the end of Chapter 3, we note further the following facts:

A. *Mountain Belts* – 1. The young mountain belts of the world are all long and continuous, the older belts are short and broken.

2. Active mountain arcs all lie *on the leading edges* of continental rafts which are presupposed to have drifted on the crest of the convection currents in the mantle into their present positions: a fact which fits neatly into the scheme of continental growth from an ancient nucleus outwards towards the edges of the proto-continents Laurasia and Gondwanaland outlined in Chapter 2.

3. The Andes chain of mountain arcs, on the leading edge of South America, are much less symmetrical than the younger island arcs off the leading edge of Asia. The explanation of this fact may well be that the Andes began as island arcs off the coast of South America *before* it

88

broke away from Gondwanaland, only to be overrun by the subsequent movement of the sub-continent westward. As Tuzo Wilson remarks: "To be thus caught up and overriden appears to be the fate of mountain arcs."

4. The switch of direction of the compressional zone of fracture on the west coast of North America from eastwards towards the Appalachians to southward towards the Andes, which, as we have already seen, occurred early in the Mesozoic era, finds its natural interpretation as one facet of the kaleidoscopic change in the convection pattern in the mantle, which on other evidence must have occurred at that time.

B. *Ocean Basins* – 1. The youth of the ocean floor in both Pacific and Atlantic and the sparseness of ocean sediments receive a simple explanation, if we suppose with Robert Dietz of San Diego in California that the ocean floors, carried on the convection currents which rise below the mid-ocean rifts, spread right and left towards the neighbouring coast-lines: where they slide downwards below the continental rafts, leaving their sediments plastered to the under surface of each raft, like crumbs swept out of sight under the carpet.

2. The *distribution* of the sediments over the total area of an ocean floor speaks to this same explanation. Thus the most recent investigations of the Lamont group, carried out in the Atlantic during the 1963 season with their latest development of seismic shooting at sea – the so-called 'continuous profiler' – tell that in the region of the Mid-Atlantic Ridge the thickness of the sediments is rarely more than a few hundred metres and that frequently the bottom is as bare of sediment as the cliff illustrated in Plate III; while the thickness increases with increasing distance from the ocean ridge and decreasing distance from the continental shelf, until it is too great to be penetrated even by the powerful sonic beam of the Lamont profiler.

MAGNETIC LOG-BOOK

Some of the most convincing early evidence for the reality of continental drift came from the close similarity, if not identity, of plant and animal fossils in geological strata of the same age in areas which are today thousands of miles apart;

89

and we shall examine some of this evidence in the sequel. All that can be deduced from such similarities, however, is that areas A and B, now x thousand miles apart, were probably contiguous y thousand million years ago: *the track on the earth's surface* followed by A and B in arriving at their present stations is pure guesswork.

There is, however, a very particular type of fossil which allows us in a measure to log the course of the drifting continents from their port of departure to their present port of call: namely *fossil magnetism*.

The new science of Paleomagnetism reads the record of the rocks with the aid of the grains of iron- or nickel-bearing substances which are frequently found frozen into the substance of once-molten lavas, or held fast in the material of sedimentary rocks which were once mobile mud or shifting sand. At the time when either lava or sandstone was laid down, we must suppose that these magnetic granules aligned themselves, and were permanently magnetised, in the direction of the earth's magnetic field appropriate to that time and place. Cemented into position when lava or sediment solidified, they are the fossilised trace of the earth's magnetic field prevailing at their original place of deposition in bygone geological areas—always provided that the rocks have not subsequently been reworked by either volcanic or igneous action.

Turn now to Fig. 1.9, and notice how a freely suspended magnetic needle, aligned in the direction of the earth's magnetic lines of force at its point of suspension, lies horizontally at the Equator, but dips — North-seeking pole downwards in the northern hemisphere, South-seeking pole downwards in the southern hemisphere — always more steeply as it approaches either pole. By measuring the angle of magnetic dip, in fact, a man can determine his *geographical latitude* without recourse to the stars.

Similarly, by measuring the angle of magnetic dip of rocks *in situ*, we can deduce their latitude at the time they were laid down, on the very reasonable assumption that the earth's magnetic field has always been the axial field it is today.

We can indeed go further, and deduce the ancient *horizontal orientation* of these same rocks – whether they were laid down north and south, or east and west; *but we can do nothing in paleomagnetism about ancient longitudes*. As Patrick Blackett of

Imperial College in London, a pioneer of paleomagnetism applied to continental drift, so succinctly puts it: "The paleomagnetist is in exactly the same position as a seaman only able to observe the altitude of the pole star. He can deduce the orientation of his ship and its latitude but can say nothing about its longitude." Thus paleomagnetism is silent on the question whether America and Europe were once nearer or further apart than they are today: the answer to that question must be sought elsewhere. But on the subject of the postulated fragmentation of Gondwanaland, the paleomagnetic evidence is dramatic.

ON COURSE FROM ANTARCTICA

Guided by convection currents in the mantle, the four continental land masses of South America, Africa, India and Australia were scheduled to set sail from the heartland of Antarctica in mid-Mesozoic times for their present anchorages: voyages of anything up to five or six thousand miles in the last two hundred million years, at a cruising speed of two or three centimetres a year. Let us consult the magnetic log which each carries, entered in the record of its rocks, so that we may chart its ancient latitudes and compass course throughout its voyage north.

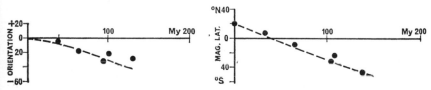

4.4. The paleomagnetic log of the voyage of India from its home port in Gondwanaland to its present anchorage in South-East Asia.

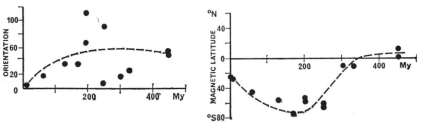

4.5. The record of Australia's voyages in the past 500 million years.

The magnetic log is most complete for India and Australia, as shown graphically in Figs. 4.4 and 4.5, and pictorially on the map of 4.6.* Australia offers its own puzzle in the *southward* drift recorded for Pre-Mesozoic times, to which we shall return later. About all we can say of South America for the present is that it hasn't altered appreciably in latitude since the Jurassic period, some 150 millions years ago; and little

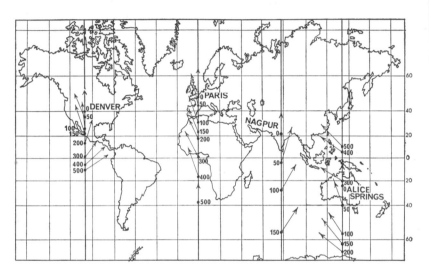

4.6. The paleomagnetic record of continental drift referred to the latitudes of the four key towns Denver, Paris, Nagpur and Alice Springs (after Blackett et al.)

more can be said of Africa. But already the entries in the magnetic logs for the fragments of old Gondwanaland are sufficiently exciting to demand an independent test.

PALEOCLIMATES IN GONDWANALAND

This test has been made in a masterly fashion by Blackett in the Proceedings of the Royal Society of London for 1961, in which he compares the ancient paleomagnetic latitudes with *the ancient climates*, as revealed chiefly by the Permo-Carboni-

* Figs. 4.4, 4.5 and 4.6 are after Blackett *et al.* (Proceedings of the Royal Society *A, 256, 291* (1960)); Figs. 4.7, 4.8 and 4.10 after Blackett (*ibid.*, A, *263*, 1 (1961)).

ferous coal measures and glaciation on the one hand, and by corals and salt deposits on the other.

Now the standard text-book picture of the Carboniferous period is one of steaming tropical swamps nurturing a forest of giant plants, of which our contemporary fronded *Equisetae* or 'horse-tails' are the miserable modern remnant. This picture however is true only for the coal-measures *of the northern hemisphere*: the coal measures in the southern hemisphere, in Australia, India, South Africa, and South America alike, carry a fossilised flora both poorer in species and comparatively stunted in growth, the most prominent of which is *Glossopteris*, a plant carrying a characteristic tongue-shaped leaf. Moreover, the southern coal measures are closely associated with intense and extensive glaciation (see Plate XVII).

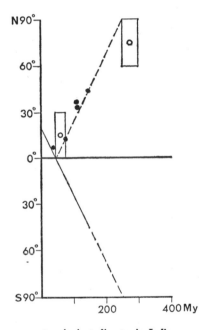

4.7. Ancient climates in India.

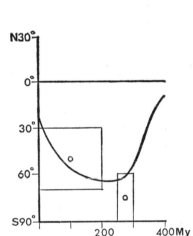

4.8. Ancient climates in Australia.

Note that in Fig. 4.7 the actual track of the northward drift of India is shown in the lower half of the diagram; the paleo-magnetic latitudes ($\bullet$), and climatic rectangles $T_1T_2 : L_1L_2$ are plotted above the 0° line for greater clarity. In Fig. 4.8 the log for Australia is restricted to the period of from zero to 400 million years ago.

93

TABLE 4.1: ANCIENT CLIMATE OF INDIA

Period	Age in millions of years between T_1 and T_2		Climatic Indicators	Climatic Zone	Range of Latitude between L_1 and L_2	
	T_1	T_2			L_1	L_2
Eocene	50	70	Salt, gypsum and corals	Equatorial and half arid	0	30
Permo-Carboniferous	250	300	Glaciation, coupled with *Glossopteris* coal measures	Polar and half temperate	60	90

TABLE 4.2: ANCIENT CLIMATE OF AUSTRALIA

Period	Age in millions of years between T_1 and T_2		Climatic Indicators	Climatic Zone	Range of Latitude between L_1 and L_2	
	T_1	T_2			L_1	L_2
Quaternary/Mesozoic	0	210	Large insects and reptiles; minor glaciations	Temperate and half arid	30	70
Permo-Carboniferous	250	400	Extensive glaciation; coal deposits	Polar and half temperate	60	90
Cambrian	370	600	Corals	Equatorial and half arid	0	30

94

The paleoclimate of the Gondwana deposits was in fact most probably wet and rather cold and it need not surprise us to find the coal measures of the southern hemisphere taken here as indicators of a *temperate* climatic zone.

Blackett applies these and other criteria of paleoclimatic zoning as indicators to the contemporary ancient latitudes, and he has made comparisons of such *paleoclimatic* latitudes L with the *paleomagnetic* latitudes λm of India, Australia, and tentatively of Africa.

The appropriate data for India are assembled in Table 4.1, and exhibited graphically in Fig. 4.7; those for Australia are set out in Table 4.2, and graphed for the first two climatic periods of Table 4.2 in Fig. 4.8. The agreement between the ancient latitudes determined by the paleomagnetic technique on the one hand, and those estimated from the paleoclimatic evidence on the other, speaks for itself.

In the case of India, there is corroborative evidence that this land mass did indeed arrive off the coast of East Asia from the south: for the Himalayas show every evidence of having begun life as an island arc bordering the paleozoic Tethys Sea; and of having subsequently been uplifted to become the highest mountains in the world by the northward thrusting pressure of India.

Australia we shall return to in the sequel.

THE HEARTLAND OF GONDWANA

A glance at Fig. 4.3(b) tells us that the heartland of old Gondwana was Antarctica: and it is in the Antarctica of today that we can best make our search for the ancient history of the southern proto-continent, and of the processes at work in its fragmentation.

Now prior to 1955, when serious preparations for the Antarctic programme of the IGY 1957–58 got under way, the Antarctic continent was visited by man only on those sporadic occasions when bold geographical explorers like Scott, Amundsen, Shackleton, Byrd landed on the pack-ice to lead their dashes for the South Pole. In the Antarctic winter of 1963, however, there was a total human population – voluntary exiles from Australia, Chile, France, New Zealand, South Africa, the U.K., the U.S.A., and last but not least the USSR – of some 500 souls.

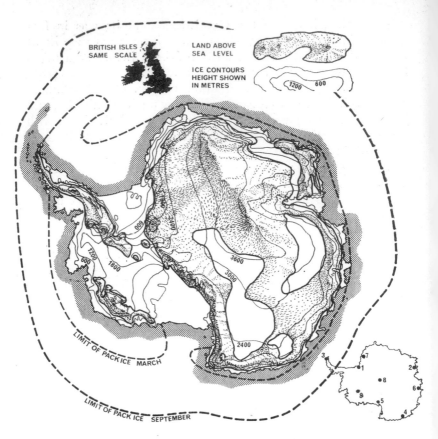

4.9. Antarctica of the Twelve Nations. Of the 35 stations active during the Antarctic winter of 1962 we show on the small map bottom right a selected nine: namely 1. Argentina (General Belgrano); 2. Australia (Mawson); 3. Chile (General Bernardo O'Higgins); 4. France (Dumont d'Urville); 5. New Zealand (Scott); 6. USSR (Mirny); 7. UK (Halley Bay); 8. USA (Amundsen-Scott South Pole); 9. USA (Byrd). The Republic of South Africa held station on the Prince Edward Islands on the Antarctic convergence of the waters of the Antarctic and Indian Oceans; Belgium and Japan were temporarily absent.

In sober truth, the *scientific exploration* of Antarctica is under way: and already in the Ohio Range of the Horlick Mountains the Americans have made geological finds which are of first importance to our present topic. Thus in the Devonian sandstones and shales they have found *in situ* fossils of bivalve shellfish and the Devonian ancestors of whelks and snails and corals. In the overlying boulder clay, or glacial tillite, dating from the

96

H.M.S. *Challenger* at St. Paul's Rocks, in Lat. 0° 55′ N, Long. 29° 22′ W, on August 28 1873.

Atlantis, for over thirty years the flagship of the fleet at Woods Hole Oceanographic Institution. This beautiful yacht-like vessel, designed by Owen and Minot of Boston, was built by Burmeister and Wain at Copenhagen in 1931.

Meteor, the research vessel of the German Hydrographic Institute which pioneered the mapping of the topography of the ocean bottom in 1925-7.

Discovery II, the sturdy all-purpose ocean-going laboratory of the British National Institute of Oceanography from her launch at Port Glasgow in November 1929 to her sale to the ship-breakers in May 1963. She is succeeded by *Discovery III*, a leading participant in the International Indian Ocean Expedition.

FOUR HISTORIC OCEAN-GOING RESEARCH VESSELS.

Plate IX

Plate X

A modern echo-sounder with its 'fish'– and the profile of the ocean floor which is being recorded in the picture by Tony Laughton . . . and they work like this:

The *echo-sounder* makes use of the 'Mufax' chart recorder manufactured by the Muirhead Company in Beckenham, Kent. Instead of the primitive stylus of the old-time echo-sounder, we have here a single-turn helical blade (rather like that you can see on your lawn-mower) rotating against a knife edge with chemically impregnated paper in between. . . . Clearly, there is always point contact between blade and paper somewhere across its width. Now when this point of contact is at that particular spot on the left-hand edge of the paper which is being firmly pinched by the helix, a 'post-office relay' closes two electrical contacts simultaneously: one allows current to pass from blade to impregnated paper, which sets up chemical reaction to produce a black mark; the other triggers the transmitter in the fish to send its pulse of ultra-sonic waves down through the water to the ocean floor. When the echo returns from the ocean bottom to the receiver, the same mechanism functions in reverse, and a black mark on the moving roll of paper records its arrival, in deep water maybe after several complete turns of the helix – but never mind, these turns are duly notched up by switch-gear which is set in train by the initial pulse from the transmitter. . . . And even the inevitable shrinkage of the damp chemically treated paper is taken care of, by depth marks which are printed off by an electrically maintained tuning fork as the paper runs virgin white off one drum onto the drum for storage and subsequent analysis of the record. Small wonder that with the exercise of all this ingenuity the timing accuracy between the instant of transmission of a pulse and the instant of reception of its echo is as high as 1 in 3,000.

The '*fish*', the guts of which is an ultra-sonic 'transceiver' (i.e., the transmitter and receiver of Fig. 3.1 built as a single unit), is towed alongside the mother vessel, in order to eliminate one of the snags of the earlier types, built-in as they were to the hull: namely, the trapping of air bubbles between hull and water when the ship was pitching in heavy seas.

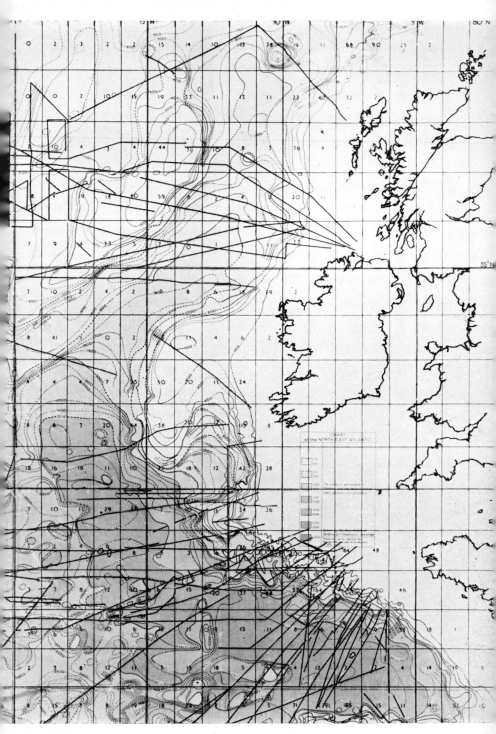

A bathymetric chart of the North Atlantic, made by Maurice Hill, voyaging in *Discovery II* in the summer of 1955. The overlay of strong black lines records the traverses made by the vessel while taking the echo-soundings which formed the basis of the chart.

Plate XI

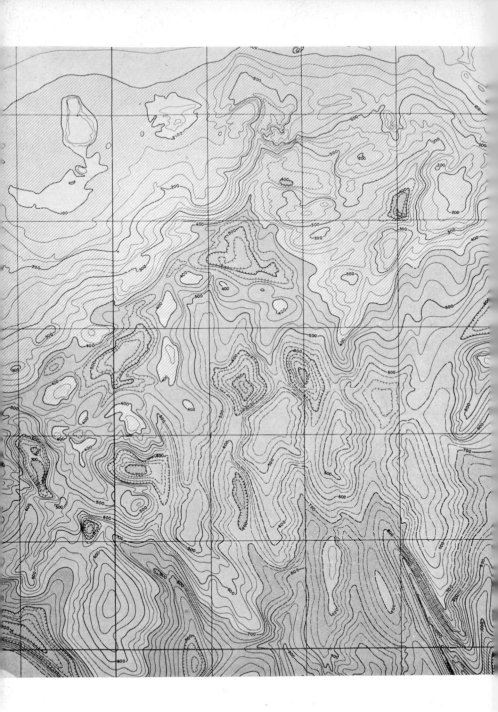

Rolling hill country at the bottom of the Gulf of Mexico off the coast of Louisiana west of New Orleans; contoured by Betty Gealy of Woods Hole Oceanographic Institute.

Plate XII

A turbidity current in action, as seen through the eye of the underwater camera.

Plate XIII

The underwater camera takes a look at the abyssal plain, 4,670 metres below the surface of the east Atlantic. The 4-inch wide track in the globigerina ooze to the left of the picture is most probably that of a holothurian or 'sea cucumber'.

Plate XIV

Plate XV

The mid-ocean rift valley comes ashore – as a 'graben' in Iceland, in Kenya as the Rift Valley.

Plate XVI

The coral polyp and its handiwork in the atolls of the Fiji group. Here in the foreground is an atoll on its way out; only the reef remains, with the wrecks of two good ships lying on its coral strand. Beyond is the coral atoll of Vatoa, all but flush with the water of its reef-encircled lagoon.

late Paleozoic era, they have found abundant remains of the flora of the southern Permo-Carboniferous forests, rich in the fossilised imprints of the fleshy-leaved *Glossopteris*, the common denominator of that period in India, Africa, and South America. And perhaps most exciting of all, they have seen in the Permian shale beds the tracks of the prehistoric free-swimming reptile the *Mesosaurus*, so richly and abundantly preserved in the Permian shales of Africa and South America.

SOUTH FROM THE EQUATOR

So far, none of the paleomagnetic evidence discussed for Gondwanaland goes further back in time than the Permo-Carboniferous. But there is one exception – Australia. And

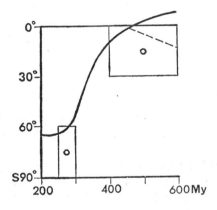

4.10. Australia's journey south in Pre-Carboniferous times.

in the case of Australia Blackett and his school can quote the evidence epitomised in Fig. 4.10, showing that 500 million years ago its latitude lay *north of the Tropic of Capricorn*; while the corresponding climatic evidence of Table 4.2 speaks of the presence of *corals* off the coasts of Mesozoic Australia.

Now today the Great Barrier Reef off the eastern coast of present-day Australia is built on a foundation of consolidated coral. Yet go back in time 100 million years and corals disappear from the record of the Australian rocks, *only to reappear over the whole period of from* 300 *to* 600 *million years ago*: in admirable corroboration of the essential accuracy of Figs. 4.8 and 4.10.

G

Further, Lowenstam of the Californian Institute of Technology has recently been tracing the *paleotemperatures* of Permian Australia, aged about 250 million years, by means of the 'O18/O16' method.

The O18/O16 method, invented by Harold Urey, then of Chicago, back in 1948, depends on the slight preference for the heavier isotope of oxygen O18 which the carbonate or lime of the shells or external skeletons of aquatic animals display in the process of their manufacture from sea water. For whereas the abundance of O18 in sea water is rather precisely 1 in 500, its abundance in organic carbonates is 1·026 in 500 at 0°C. But *as the temperature of the surrounding water rises*, so does the concentration of O18 fall: thus at 25°C it is 1·022 in 500.

This makes it possible to construct a *temperature scale* based on the ratio of O18 to the lighter isotope O16 (as determined by a refined form of the familiar mass spectrograph) in the calcareous shells or skeletons of fossil organisms, including the coral polyp.

And what does Lowenstam find when he applies this method to the fossils of Permian Australia, but a rapid rise of temperature, from 7°C to at least 13°C over a period of several million years. Look once again at Fig. 4.10, and see how this fits in with the rapid decrease in latitude as we go back in time from the minimum on the curve.

Do we glimpse here the third phase of the adjustment of earth's chameleon crust to the pattern of the convection cells in the mantle, the n=3 of Fig. 4.2? Is in fact Australia the 'marker' for the southward drift of Gondwanaland as a whole which that picture demands?

LAURASIA DRIFTS NORTH

What of Laurasia? Is there evidence that the lands of Europe and America came north from the Equator in Pre-Mesozoic times?

One very specific answer to this question comes from the study by Runcorn and Opdyke of *paleo-winds* – fossil winds whose traces are imprinted on the aeolian sandstones of the United States.

Most of us have seen and admired the beautiful contours

TABLE 4.3: ANCIENT CLIMATES OF EUROPE AND NORTH AMERICA

Age in millions of years between T_1 and T_2		Climatic Zone		λm (Europe)	Range of Latitude between L_1 and L_2				λm (USA)
T_1	T_2	Europe	USA		Europe L_1	L_2	USA L_1	L_2	
0	35	Temperate and polar		46	45	90			
35	180	Arid and equatorial		33	0	45			
180	270	Arid	Arid	17	15	45	15	45	30
270	350	Equatorial	Equatorial	5	0	15	0	15	5
350	400	Equatorial and half arid	Equatorial and half arid	5	0	30	0	30	5
400	600	Arid and temperate		21	15	70			

99

carved by the sea winds on the sand-dunes in-shore: some of us have been lucky enough to have seen and heard the true aeolian sand-hills of the North African desert. Just such ripple-marks and downwind accumulation of the sands have been found frozen into the dune sandstones of the Colorado plateau, and in Utah and Wyoming – witnesses to the direction of the prevailing surface winds of the late Cambrian. And their direction, inscribed on rocks now some five thousand miles distant from the Equator, is that of the trade-wind belt of the northern hemisphere!

4.11. Paleo-winds in the ancient aeolian sand-dunes of Arizona (after Opdyke and Runcorn).

The general *climatic* evidence for a northward drift of both North America and Europe has been assembled by Blackett. This is perhaps best exhibited, with a great saving in words, once again by means of a Table (4.3). Follow this Table on your globe with the aid of Fig. 4.6, and see how convincingly the paleomagnetic latitudes chart the northward journey.

LAURASIA SPLITS NORTH AND SOUTH

The northward drift of this great land mass on a spherical earth would soon put an intolerable strain on the earth's crust in this area, apart altogether from the birth of the 'Atlantic' convection cell. There is good reason, in fact, to accept the evidence that Laurasia split into two parts – now North America and Europe – back in the Mesozoic period. But as Du

4.12. The 'Cabot Fault' off the east coast of North America (after Tuzo Wilson).

Toit has pointed out, it is much more difficult to trace the rupture and subsequent westward and eastward drift of North America and Europe than is the case with the break-up of Gondwanaland, owing to the absence of sufficiently long base-lines on the eastern and western coasts of these continents.

THE CABOT FAULT AND THE GREAT GLEN

However, Tuzo Wilson has recently come to the rescue with a remarkable piece of detective work, which links the Cabot Fault of Eastern North America with the Great Glen, or

'Glen Mor' of the Scottish Highlands. And here is his evidence:

Canadian geologists have long been familiar with a narrow belt of transcurrent faults off the east coast of North America: namely the large fault which forms the eastern side of the Northern Peninsula in Newfoundland; the faults which have been clearly mapped in northern Cape Breton Island, in Nova Scotia, across the isthmus from Cape George to Cape Chignecto; hints that the latter fault extends beyond the Bay of Fundy to one which is known to lie off the coast of New Brunswick. It is to the credit of Tuzo Wilson that he has collated all these facts, and demonstrated that we are dealing here with segments of one great transcurrent fault, which he has named the Cabot Fault.

Now Glen Mor is the Paleozoic contemporary of the Cabot Fault: its rocks are similar, its strike is similar, and the horizontal shift of the rocks on the left-hand side of the fault relative to those on the right is in the same sense and of comparable magnitude. Wilson therefore suggests that prior to the break-up of Laurasia they were the two ends of the same fault; and indeed, if you transport a template of Scotland, with the Great Glen marked upon it, across the Atlantic, you find that it does indeed fit the northern end of the Cabot Fault, *provided that you rotate your template clockwise through 30° in agreement with Fig. 4.6.*

THE NORTH ATLANTIC FAN

Another line of geological evidence for the north-south rupture of Laurasia, stressed by Tuzo Wilson, leads us to put a close-up of the North Atlantic under the magnifying glass of orogeny.

The point of initiation of the Mid-Atlantic rift lies in the New Siberian Islands in the Arctic basin. As with any progressive fracture in any material, the rift widens as it marches south. This means that the North Atlantic, way back in the closing years of the Mesozoic period, opened out like a fan, with the pivot of the fan in the New Siberian Islands. On the farther side of the islands, therefore, lies the mirror image of the North Atlantic fan, but a fan whose leaves were flicked together by the fingers of a compensatory compression in the earth's crust. The result is there for all to see in the Verkhoyansk Mountains

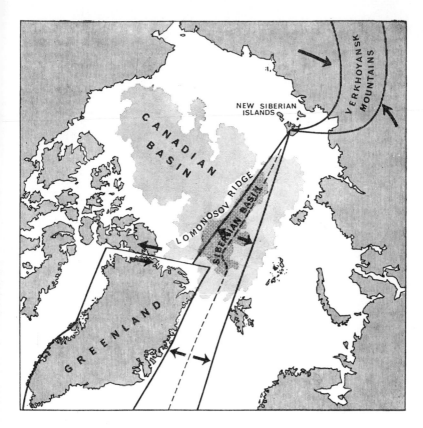

4.13. Glimpses of the mechanism of the fragmentation of Laurasia into North America and Eurasia – a fracture, marked by the scar of the Mid-Atlantic rift, which pivoted about a point in the New Siberian Islands. On the opposite side of the pivot, the tension in the earth's crust evidenced by the Rift Valley becomes the compression which raised the Verkhoyansk Mountains of Northern Siberia (after Tuzo Wilson).

of Northern Siberia, which Soviet geologists have recently dated as late Mesozoic.

AGE GROUPS AMONG THE ATLANTIC ISLANDS

Evidence in corroboration of the purely geological arguments for the separation of Europe and America is furnished by the radio-active dating of the islands in the Atlantic east and west of the Atlantic Ridge collated by Tuzo Wilson. For look at Fig. 4.14, and see how the younger isles like the Azores –

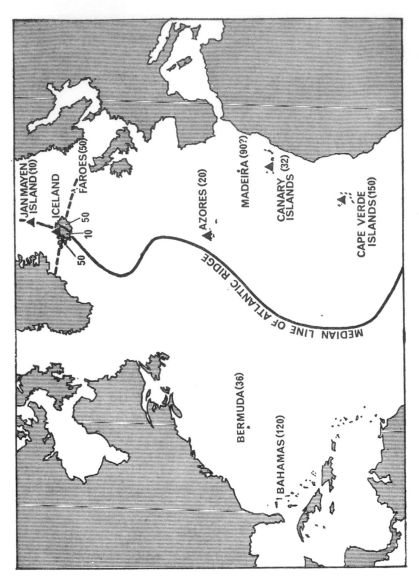

4.14. The islands in the North Atlantic are the older the farther removed they are from the Mid-Atlantic Ridge (after Tuzo Wilson).

aged 20 million years – lie close in to the ridge, while the older islands, like the Cape Verde group – 150 million years old – lie farther away from it. Indeed, an almost visual impression of the spread of the ocean floor east and west of the Atlantic Ridge is gained by brooding on this picture.

We have traced the evidence for continental drift during the last 500 million years – from the transition between Phase 3 and Phase 4 in Fig. 4.2 through Phase 4 to the present day. Phase 3 saw the drift of Gondwanaland south and of Laurasia north; Phase 4 witnessed the break-up of Gondwanaland and the fission of Laurasia: all guided by the appropriate currents in the mantle.

There remains the conundrum of the north polar land mass in the picture of Phase 4 in Fig. 4.2: and, remarkably enough, the very latest evidence points to the Arctic Ocean as not a true ocean at all but a sunken continental landmass!

Thus the floor of the Arctic basin is covered with an exceptionally thick layer of sediment, in contradistinction to that of the world ocean. Moreover, the Arctic ridges show none of the mantle-borne characteristics of the great ocean ridges of Fig. 3.9: the Lomonosov Ridge, discovered by Soviet scientists in 1948, appears as a folded system of sedimentary strata; while the Alpha Ridge, traced from the United States drifting ice station during the IGY, is revealed as an intrusion of upthrust crystalline rocks. And both formations are dated as Mid-Mesozoic.

THE LAST PHASE

The surface features of our globe now closely approach the final pattern $n = 5$: and should do so completely in the course of another ten million years or so, when *all* the iron has gone from the mantle into the core. Since, however, we and our descendants live in an age marking the final stage of the *transition* from $n = 4$ to $n = 5$, we and they must be prepared for a restless crust and mantle, turning and twisting like a dog upon the hearth before it settles down to sleep. The contemporary catastrophes in Persia, Italy, Morocco, Chile, Yugoslavia are all part of this story of the final adaptation of the earth's crust to the ultimate pattern of convection cells in the mantle.

But there are at least two other signs, less readily visible, which point in the same direction. Both are to be found in the Pacific basin.

The whole Pacific basin is twisting, anti-clockwise to the surrounding land masses. This conclusion has been reached by Hugo Benioff of Pasadena in California as a result of his study of the large transcurrent faults on land which are at once the cause and the indelible record of major earthquake shocks in the earth's crust. All the faults to be described below are *transcurrent* – that is, the slippage of one side of the fault against the other is horizontal. And they are all *dextral* – that is, a horizontal line drawn across the fault appears to rotate *clockwise*.

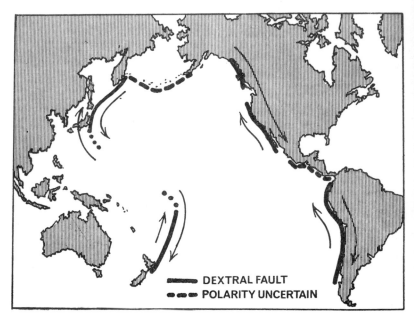

4.15. Evidence accrues that the Pacific Ocean of today is 'doing the twist' (after Benioff).

The great San Francisco quake of 1906 arose from slippage in a segment of the San Andreas fault, that classic example of a vertical transcurrent fault, which marches across the country from the Gulf of California in the south to Point Arena in the north. It is a dextral fault.

Earthquakes in Peru and Ecuador are part of the day's

work. A series of four successive deep earthquakes in the year 1915 were sufficient to establish the fact that they arose from slippage in a segment of the coastal transcurrent fault – which is dextral.

The Kamchatka earthquake of November 4 1952 allowed a detailed study of slippage in the Kuril segment of the Pacific boundary. Again the fault is found to be dextral.

And finally, the catastrophic quake of May 22 1960 in Chile: cause, slippage along the line of the coastal fault – dextral transcurrent.

Piercing together all this evidence, we arrive at the picture of Fig. 4.15: one of the entire floor of the Pacific Ocean twisting anticlockwise relative to its continental boundaries, striving on a spherical earth to adapt its topology to the most recent motions of the continental rafts: motions governed by convection cells in the mantle which are not spherical at all, but toroidal.

CRACKS IN THE FLOOR OF THE PACIFIC

It has been known for years that three big faults – Murray, Pioneer, and Mendocino – break off at right angles to the most northerly segment of the San Andreas fault, to run for miles athwart the ocean bottom of the eastern Pacific.

In the last few years, this area of the ocean bottom has been mapped for its *magnetic characteristics* by Vacquier and his colleagues from 'Scripps' at La Jolla. The beautiful patterns which they obtained of the total intensity of magnetisation of the basalt floor are shown in Fig. 4.16 – strikingly reminiscent of the strain patterns which appear in plastic materials under transverse stress.

The important practical feature of these magnetic patterns is that with them as guide it is possible to measure *the total lateral displacement* along the line of three transcurrent faults: and the answer is around 1,000 miles.

Vacquier goes a little further, and poses the question as to the *rate* of slippage along the fault lines. This turns out to be of the order of 1 cm. a year – of the same order, that is, as the speed of drift of the fragments of Gondwanaland north from the Antarctic circle . . . Here then if further evidence of the strain put upon the earth's crust in its final transition to the pattern of continent versus ocean obtaining today.

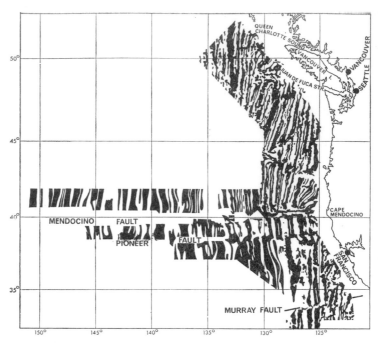

4.16. Patterns of strain in the floor of the East Pacific, as revealed by the ship's magnetometer of the Scripps expedition under Vacquier.

THE EAST PACIFIC RISE

This is our last example of earth's work-in-progress towards the finalisation of the ultimate stable mode of convection currents in the mantle, and of the distribution of land and sea at the earth's surface.

The current atop the southern sub-equatorial convection cell, flowing east from the East Pacific Rise, meets the westward current from the Mid-Atlantic Ridge in the zone of compression beneath the Andes, uplifting them in all their volcanic activity: a system which has probably held sway in this area since Cretaceous times, or even earlier. The situation East of the Isthmus of Panama, however, is quite different: for here the *downward* current of the Jurassic era has been replaced since the Cretaceous by the *upward* current of the present-day pattern. Such a reversal of sign would be expected to produce a movement of the North American continent *westward* in relation to South America: hence the shear-faults of the Carib-

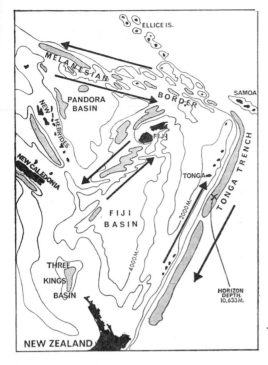

4.17. Shear-faults in the sunken Melanesian Plateau, further evidence of the current unrest in the earth's crust (after Fairbridge).

bean – and indeed Murray, Pioneer and Mendocino to the north.

On the other side of the East Pacific rise, the current flow is to the north-west. On the westward border of the Pacific basin it meets the south-eastward flow from the northern segment of the Mid-Atlantic Ridge. Hence the island arcs off the east Asian coast; and hence finally the westward movement of the southern margin of the Pacific basin past the sunken Melanesian plateau: which, clashing with the *eastward* trend of the same area in the Jurassic-Cretaceous, has stressed the crust to its limit. The resulting strain is clearly evident in the shearing which has been observed among others by Rhodes Fairbridge of Columbia in New York, between the Philippines and New Zealand.

THE TOPOGRAPHY OF THE FINAL PHASE n=5

It is fitting that the keystone on the arch of the rising convection currents in the mantle should have been set in place by the man who started the whole business back in the twenties, Vening-Meinesz: who was so far ahead of his time in his proposals that today bright young men rediscover his fundamental discoveries and think quite sincerely that these are their own.

The pictures of Fig. 4.2 showing the correlation between the convection pattern in the mantle and the distribution of the earth's land masses are admittedly crude. Vening-Meinesz, however, at the age of seventy-plus, has carried out a remarkable piece of team-work in his native Holland which demonstrates in detail just how closely the present topography of the globe is linked to the contemporary 'fifth mode' governing the convection currents in the mantle.

In the first place G. J. Bruins of Delft, a one-time pupil of Vening-Meinesz, supplied with the help of his staff a total of 40,680 contour diagrams of the elevation of the earth's surface at as many places on the globe. Next, the Mathematical Centre in Amsterdam carried out the laborious computation of the corresponding 'spherical harmonics' such as would be reflected by a hypothetical convection pattern in the mantle of no less than 31 convection cells, large and small, the predominance of one or more of which over the others in the total convection pattern should be reflected in the surface topography. And finally Vening-Meinesz himself correlated the results.

It turns out that the chief topographical feature of the globe, its division into land and sea, is due almost entirely *to the first five terms* in the harmonic analysis, in complete agreement with Runcorn's theoretical deductions. But there is more to it than that.

Thus the analysis reflects the most prominent feature of the surface topography of the earth – the land hemisphere to the north, the sea hemisphere to the south of the Equator. It reveals the presence of a world-wide range of undersea mountains, which would have sent even the shore-based oceanographers to sea if the echo-sounder had not already discovered them. And it shows up most beautifully (in the 26th harmonic!) the subsidiary ocean basins of the island arc systems, such as the Philippine Sea and the Banda basin in the Indonesian Archipelago – and gives more than a hint that there are others still to be discovered. It is a fairly safe bet that if a small international group of our leading deep-sea oceanographers and marine geologists were to get together to make a detailed fundamental examination of the work of their Dutch colleagues, invaluable guide-lines towards those areas of the ocean floor which would repay fresh or further study would be laid down.

CHAPTER 5

Sea and Sky

IN the three preceding chapters we have surveyed the evolution of the continental blocks of the earth's crust, and the changing topography of the ocean bottom; we have recognised two great fracture lines in the earth's crust – that of the mountain arcs a zone of compression, that of the mid-ocean rift a zone of tension; we have seen how these are the outward and visible signs of the inward and invisible convection currents in the mantle, and how these convection currents directed the continents to their present stations and shaped the ocean basins as we know them today.

But the predominant role of the mantle in determining the earth's surface features doesn't end there: the air we breathe and the water we sail upon are also its offspring. All the water in the ocean was once volcanic steam; the earth's atmosphere – four parts nitrogen to one of oxygen – was once the ammonia, methane, and carbon dioxide belched forth from the world's volcanoes in Pre-Cambrian times.

Take the water first. The old story ran that torrents of rain fell upon the earth as it cooled and shrank from its pristine state as a fiery ball under a black sky – the tale of the puckered orange skin and the super-saturated atmosphere, in fact. Such a picture of past events is of course flatly contradicted by our present knowledge, namely that the composition of proto-earth was originally that of its parent sun, but that it *lost* almost all of its primeval atmosphere, and that in two distinct stages: first on account of the solar wind, blowing through space some 5,000 million years ago from the new-born incandescent sun; second, because the lighter components of its remaining gases got shot off like slugs from a catapult, around 4,500 million years ago, from the spinning atmospheric bulge at the Equator, which was then rotating perhaps nearly ten times as fast as it is today, when proto-earth's youthful speed of rotation has been slowed down to its present middle-aged pace by the tidal drag of the moon. This second phase we know about because the quantities of such primeval gases as neon and krypton present today in the earth's atmosphere are only one hundred thousand millionth and one tenth of a millionth respectively of the proportional amounts present in the sun. No, Noah's flood came considerably later in the march of time.

However, if we compare the amount of water vapour emitted by all the volcanoes in the world since the beginning of geological time with the total volume of water present in the oceans, just as we did for the lavas and solid continents in Chapter 2, then we find that the two figures tally tolerably well at five million million cubic feet. Moreover, the *composition* of sea water points to a volcanic origin: its content of chlorides in particular – its saltiness, in other words – would be difficult to account for except as arising from the solution of the hydrochloric acid gas which accompanies the other gaseous hydrides in the eruption of lava from volcanoes.

Next, the atmosphere. The gases spewed out by volcanoes are predominantly *hydrides*, molecules of a small variety of chemical elements – nitrogen, carbon, oxygen – combined with hydrogen.

The production of the nitrogen and oxygen of our present-day atmosphere, therefore, was a *secondary* process, brought about by the photochemical decomposition of ammonia and water vapour by ultra-violet radiation coming from the sun: whereby the light mobile hydrogen atoms and hydrogen molecules escaped into outer space, leaving the heavier oxygen and nitrogen entrapped in the gravitational field of the earth. The methane fraction, too, would be photochemically decomposed; leaving behind carbon, ready to combine with the newly born oxygen to form CO_2.

But now comes a truly astonishing fact – that if you make a mixture of NH_3, H_2O, and CH_4 in the laboratory, and then subject your mixture to the ionising and photochemical action of an electric discharge, you find that you have produced *amino-acids*, universally recognised as the backbone of the protein molecules which are the basic material of all living cells.

H

Moreover, *nucleic acids*, such as are the vertebrae as it were in the spinal column of the giant molecule of deoxyribonucleic acid ('DNA' for short) which tells the amino-acids in the living cell what proteins they must assemble in order to make a mouse or a man, a louse or a lion: these have been synthesised by Shramm of Tubingen in Germany from a broth of simple sugars, amino-acids and the submolecules of DNA known as *nucleotides*: all of them substances which could have been formed on a lifeless earth under the same conditions of temperature and pressure as characterised the primeval oceans.

And now, in 1963, Cyril Ponnamperuma and his associates at the University of California have actually succeeded in synthesising one of these DNA nucleotides – adenine – from a mixture of methane ammonia and water, under the bombardment of a beam of electrons of energy comparable to that of the cosmic rays from outer space which streak through the earth's atmosphere to penetrate the outer skin of the crust, particularly the upper layer of the oceans.

Next: the rate of production of oxygen from water vapour by the ultra-violet radiation from the sun is much too slow to convert to carbon dioxide *all* the carbon monoxide which has been pouring out into the atmosphere, since the beginning of geological time, from all the volcanoes of the world. It is clear that until this conversion was complete, any free oxygen in the atmosphere soon found itself imprisoned in a molecule of CO_2.

So on this basis there could be no free oxygen in the earth's atmosphere *until there were plants on the earth's surface to release it.* In other words, the dawn of life on earth arose around a thousand million years ago with the formation from the primeval atmosphere and oceans of the first proteins and nucleotides: and the air we breathe today is itself a product of living organisms, in addition to those products arising from the purely mechanical processes of volcanic action beneath the earth's crust.

The earth's atmosphere and oceans, then, are as much a part of the earth we live on as its solid crust. Together they function as one great heat engine, powered by the sun, that conditions climate and weather, ocean waves and currents. The horsepower of the ocean-atmosphere heat engine is prodigious – two thousand million million horse-power. Its working fluid is water vapour, the winds of heaven its moving parts, the slow circulation of the oceans in their basins its massive flywheel.

Besides, the planetary heat engine is equipped with a colossally powerful 'feed-back' mechanism – its 'governor' in other words. No sooner does it begin to run too fast than restraining influences immediately leap into operation: too slow, and accelerating agents take over.

This all-important characteristic of the circulation cycles of atmosphere and oceans is at once a pedagogic headache and a mathematical nightmare: for the question it poses, alike to the expositor and the back-room boy who is struggling to understand them, is always the same: Where shall we begin?

Now the myriad readers of that admirable author Mr. Somerset Maugham know full well that all stories should be like those he can write best himself: they should have a beginning, a middle, and an end. Unfortunately, the blueprint of the planetary heat-engine is inscribed on a cylinder – you can begin reading it anywhere you like. As George Deacon, Director of the British National Institute of Oceanography, has put it: "Do the trade winds give rise to the Gulf Stream, or is the Gulf Stream responsible for the trade winds?"

So in the sequel, in which we shall meet this difficulty time and time again, it is well to remember that reading about climate and weather, winds and waves, is rather like a first attempt at understanding the philosophy of Immanuel Kant, about which beginners are often warned that they can only apprehend it as a complete whole. . . .

The power house of the atmospheric heat engine is the sun. Each minute the sun radiates energy equivalent to the output of an electric heater rated at one billion quadrillion kilowatts. The earth intercepts but a small fraction (a circular sample of area πr_e^2, where r_e is the earth's radius) of this enormous total – about ten billionths, to be exact. This catch is distributed in virtue of the rotation of the earth over the earth's spherical surface of $4\pi r_e^2$: so that the initial input of solar radiation at the boundary of the earth's atmosphere is effectively reduced to one quarter of its incident value. Nevertheless, there remains $1 \cdot 6 \times 10^{15}$ kilowatts, or if you like 2×10^{15} horse-power, to drive the winds and the waves, to evaporate sea water to give us rain, to disintegrate the exposed rocks of mountain peaks and glacial shields, to pulverise the soil of the plains and valleys, to maintain the photosynthetic life of all plants, and to set in motion through photosynthesis by the microscopic algae in the surface waters of the oceans – the 'grass' of the sea pastures – the many-linked chain of life in the waters under the earth: herbivorous sub-microscopic diatoms and radiolaria, flesh-eating shrimps and copepods, small breeds of squids, and finally edible fishes like cod, halibut and tunny.

Now it is clear that the earth must radiate this captured energy back into space at exactly the same rate at which it receives it: otherwise the temperature of the earth would not be maintained at the steady average level we recognise as our world climate. This comes about through a rather complicated mechanism, conditioned by four chief factors: the oxygen in the upper atmosphere, the ozone layer that lies some 15 miles high above earth, the earth's cloud cover, and the presence throughout the lower reaches of the atmosphere of water and carbon dioxide in the proportions of 2 per cent and 3 hundredths of a per cent respectively.

The role of both the high level oxygen content and the ozone layer of the upper atmosphere in the present context is very similar: put briefly, they absorb almost completely all electro-magnetic radiation from the sun shorter in wavelength than one hundred thousandth of an inch. Expressed rather more fully, this means that the energy in the ultra-violet end of the sun's spectrum which arrives at the top of the atmosphere is entirely expended: first, in the ionisation of the high-lying oxygen, thus helping to form the ionosphere, the reflector of man-made radio-waves; second, in the photo-chemical decomposition of tri-atomic oxygen, ozone (O_3), into ordinary oxygen (O_2) and atomic oxygen (O).

Now studies of the ionosphere, or of the queer chemistry of the upper atmosphere, are outside the scope of this book. But we note here that it is not only the oxygen we breathe that makes life on earth as we know it possible; for a hundred miles high in the rarefied ionosphere and 15 miles high in the ozone layer it filters out the lethal shorter ultra-violet rays from the sun, only yielding passage to the longer ultra-violet rays, the kind which give us that Riviera sun-tan.

The effect of the clouds is very simple. Anyone who has looked down on them from an air-liner knows how white they are as seen from above. In the language of Physics, they are tolerably efficient reflectors of the light incident upon them: or to be exact, they are responsible for no less than 25 per cent of the total outgoing radiation from the earth.

What of the remaining 75 per cent? Close on 10 per cent is 'back-scattered' – from water droplets, dust particles, the very molecules of the air itself. The remaining 65 per cent goes out through a tiny little skylight in the earth's greenhouse without glass.

This is where the water vapour and carbon dioxide in the earth's atmosphere play their part. Both are transparent to the visible radiation from the sun, but together are very nearly opaque to all but a small portion of the infra-red region of the spectrum.

Now the narrow wave-band, lying almost solely in the visible part of the sun's spectrum, which actually strikes the earth's surface, land and sea alike, as approximately half of the total solar radiation incident at the top of the atmosphere, warms the land and the upper skin of the oceans so that they radiate, like any warm object, not in the visible but in the infra-red.

But only in the narrow region lying between the absorption bands of water vapour and carbon-dioxide can the infra-red radiation of the sun-warmed earth escape back into space. Here then is your 'greenhouse effect', the thermal regulator if you like, which ultimately sets the average temperature of the earth, and holds it at a steady world average over the years.

It is well at this point to stress the words 'world average value'; for clearly there are local fluctuations about that average, both seasonal and latitudinal: it is only the overall figure of the earth's surface temperature which gives a steady reading on the planetary thermometer.

This is well shown in Fig. 5.1, where the daily insolation, in arbitrary units 0 to 6, is plotted against latitude vertically and through the four seasons horizontally. We may read many important statements in this graphical expression of thousands of careful measurements. Thus:

1. The polar caps reflect almost all the solar radiation falling on them; in fact, during the Arctic and Antarctic winters they are practically perfect reflectors;

2. The heavy cloud cover over the Equator reflects so strongly that the areas of maximum insolation lie not on the geographical Equator, but to the north and south of it;

3. The areas of maximum insolation north and south of the Equator are not symmetrically located – insolation is more intense in the sub-tropical regions *south* of the Equator, because of the vastly greater area of poorly reflecting ocean water, as against that of the better reflecting land masses, which is a characteristic of the geography of the southern hemisphere.

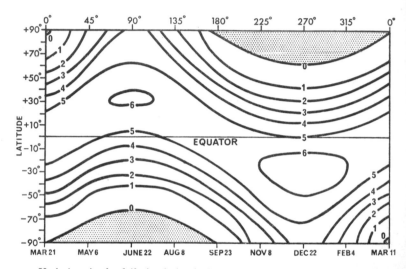

5.1. Variations in the daily insolation both in latitude and through the four seasons of the year (after Hauritz).

We recognise in Fig. 5.1 the boiler and condenser of the atmospheric heat engine; namely the sub-tropical seas and the ice-caps over the poles. Thus a transfer of high-grade heat must be looked for from the Equator to the poles, the return of low-grade heat from the poles to the Equator: the 'steam' and 'condenser water' in fact of the familiar steam engine.

Now we have already stated baldly that the working fluid of the ocean-atmosphere heat engine is water vapour. How then is the heat engine fuelled? Answer: by the trade-wind clouds.

Anyone who has voyaged from London to the Cape, or from New York to Rio, has spent many peaceful hours watching the cloud galleons of the Trades as they sail before the wind, at first south, then later on towards the north, but always towards the Equator. Few realise that they are large-scale fuel pumps, raising water evaporated from the surface of the sea – in the northern hemisphere in the Caribbean or off Cape Verde, in the southern hemisphere off Porto Alegre and Walvis Bay – injecting it high into the warm air stream of the Trades.

The trade-wind clouds, in fact, are launched in the areas of maximum insolation depicted in Fig. 5.1. In these warm sub-tropical seas, the air above the water is particularly dry, for a good reason which will be made clear in the sequel. Straight-forward evaporation of water vapour from the surface of the ocean into the ambient air is therefore here at a maximum.

Water vapour crosses the sea/air interface, however, but rarely in a simple evaporation process from a flat surface, as in an inland lake. The rapid evaporation of spray, thrown up by the trade-winds themselves, has come to be recognised as a very important factor in the transfer of water vapour from oceans to atmosphere. Moreover, the *rate* of evaporation waxes and wanes with the roughly mondial cycle of the growth and decay of sub-tropical anticyclones, in tune with the meander-ings of the polar jet-stream which we shall meet in the sequel: for when these sub-tropical anticyclones are at the peak of their development, the surface flow of the Trades becomes intense; and the air they transport is more than particularly dry, as it invariably is in a region of high pressure. In short, conditions are then at their optimum for rapid evaporation.

Thus the injection of water vapour into the working cycle of the atmospheric heat-engine takes place in spurts, spaced fairly regularly at intervals of from three to five weeks. The trade wind clouds, in other words, visit always the same filling stations, but are not invariably supplied with the same number of gallons. And you can actually see this reflected in their shape and form: now small and stunted, now towering giants (see Plate XX).

But whatever the mechanism and rate of evaporation of water vapour from the ocean may be, one constant physical process rules throughout: namely, that not only must the temperature of the water be raised to the evaporation point by the heat of the sun, but an *additional* amount of heat must be injected – the so-called *latent heat of evaporation* – as when we bring a domestic kettle to the boil. It is in fact the latent heat of evaporation in sea water, later released into the upper atmosphere, which is the source of energy that drives the planetary winds (and ocean currents, as we shall see in due course): just as in the familiar steam engine.

A certain fraction of the total amount of latent heat transferred from sea to air over the sub-tropical seas goes to drive the fuel pumps of the trade-wind clouds themselves. Studies from specially equipped aircraft of the tall chimney-shaped clouds have shown that they are in a constant state of growth, mostly to windward, with a corresponding secular decay down wind: giving rise to a turbulent circulation within each cloud which pumps water vapour upwards from the intake near sea-level to the output at a height of 7,000 feet or more. In their passage to the Equator, either from the north or from the south, the trade-wind clouds constantly inject enormous quantities of water vapour, night and day, into the ever-warmer air stream of the Trades.

Arrived at the Equator, the warm moist air from the north converges with the trade winds of the southern hemisphere, and is swept aloft, carrying the clouds with it. In its ascent to the cold regions of the higher atmosphere, its water vapour is jettisoned, to fall in sheets of tropical rain on land and sea below. At the same time, the solar energy it has held entrapped as latent heat during its journey south is released, to drive the whole planetary wind system.

Let us follow now the track of the trade winds from their starting points 30° north or south of the Equator. They begin as winds driving due south or due north, as the case may be, from the dry areas of high pressure in the Horse Latitudes. Gradually however they alter course, from due south to south-west or from due north to north-west: for they are winds which must obey the deflecting force of a spinning earth – always to the right of their direction of motion, as we shall soon learn. Converging at the Equator, they are forced to sweep vertically upwards, until at 20,000 feet or so above earth they find themselves constituting a girdle around the earth of air at relatively high pressure. Thence, they spread north and south in a complex pattern of swirls and eddies, until they come against the sub-tropical jet streams, high up under the roof of the earth's lower atmosphere – the so-called troposphere. Here the air is cold, dry and heavy; it sinks earthward to resume the cycle, east of the Bermudas or south of the Canaries as the case may be.

We have traced the boundaries of the *trade-wind cells*, sometimes called the Hadley cells after their discoverer George Hadley, eighteenth-century British astronomer, the circulation in which is *meridianal* (see Plate XXI).

Contrary to the chart of the planetary winds drawn up in the days of sail, which proposed two further meridianal circulation cells in each hemisphere to account for the westerlies in the north and south temperate zones and the prevailing easterlies within the Arctic and Antarctic Circles, the air age now recognises the trade-wind cell as the only example of straight meridianal circulation in the earth's atmosphere. For north of 30°N and south of 30°S the winds blow *zonally*, in two great vortices around the poles as centre.

Let us concentrate our attention for the moment on the northern system, lying between latitudes 80°N and 30°N, at an average height of 20,000 feet.

The core of the north polar vortex of winds is the polar jet stream, discovered in latitude 60°N during World War II by high-flying long distance bombers of the U.S. Air Force. The polar jet stream is no tame river of air: it is a rushing mighty wind, concentrated in an aerial funnel only 300 miles wide and 3 miles high, roaring around the roof of the world with a speed of 200 m.p.h. or more at a height of 30,000 feet above ground. Its influence is felt down as far as 10,000 feet, the lower limit of the so-called geostrophic winds that trace out the great circles of the globe between the Arctic Circle and 30°N.

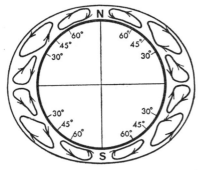

5.2. *The chart of the planetary winds current in the days of sailing ships, which showed three separate meridianal circulation cells in each hemisphere. The air age recognises only the trade-wind cells as valid: north and south of these, zonal circulation predominates.*

5.3. Three stages in the breakdown of the geostrophic phase of the polar jet stream. In the final stage, a turbulent exchange of hot and cold air between the subtropics and the north polar region is effected, which goes to assure the transport of heat from the Equator to the Pole, and its return, downgraded, to the Equator: a cycle which must be maintained if the atmospheric heat-engine is to be kept steadily in motion.

But wait a bit! Are we going too fast and too far? Is the jet stream indeed Prospero commanding, or is he rather obedient Ariel running his master's errands on the sharp winds of the north? Here indeed we are squarely faced with the feed-back riddle: and we can only answer that it's true either way, but that the way we've put it is fair enough for didactic purposes.

That word of warning having been given, let us proceed: Faced with a *zonal* circulation of winds aloft, centred on the polar jet stream, how can we account for the interchange of warm and cold air (so majestically achieved in the trade-wind meridianal cell between Equator and 30°N), between 30°N. and the Pole?

The answer comes as the result of an intensive experimental and theoretical investigation, carried out during the forties of the present century under the inspired direction of one man – Carl Gustav Rossby, hard-living, hard-working Swede who burned himself out to die in 1957 at the age of fifty-nine.

And here is his answer: The polar jet stream is a black sheep, unlike its brothers, the sub-tropical jet streams above the Horse Latitudes, which pursue their even way around the world year in and year out. As much as a month at a time, the polar jet stream behaves as any well-conducted geostrophic wind should, obeying the eastward spin of the earth, piling up pressure to the right of its direction of motion, holding to its circular track about the Pole. But at intervals of three to five weeks, sometimes even longer, intervals which are meantime unpredictable to man, it breaks loose. It lashes itself into great loops, 4,000 miles or more across, dragging the whole circumpolar vortex with it, thrusting cold air from the north south to the tropics, hauling warm air north from the Caribbean. And it is in this untidy way of Fig. 5.3 that the interchange of warm and cold air between the sub-tropics and the polar regions is accomplished.

This Walpurgisnacht in the upper atmosphere is staged between 10,000 and 30,000 feet. What of the corresponding conditions near the earth's surface?

To those of us who live along the eastern borders of the North Sea, this is a very pertinent question. For the answer is this: During a period of rebellion on the part of the jet stream, cold dry air lying above Northern Canada can be pulled southward behind the trough of an eastward advancing wave in the scalloped edge of the polar vortex, warm air from the Carribbean can be sucked into the rearward edge of the next northward-probing crest. The two air masses meet in a turbulent struggle on the western seabord of the Atlantic – and the birth of a whole family of cyclones is announced on the lower slopes of the polar vortex.

And in due course the separate members of the cyclone family leave the parental hearth: circular currents of air flowing against the clock, they drift eastward across the Atlantic as the 'depressions' which the western European knows only too well.

So much for zonal circulation in the atmosphere polewards of 30° N. Now for 'hot news' from Antarctica.

Next to nothing was known about the atmosphere of Antarctica before that *annus mirabilis* 1957, the year of the IGY, when no fewer than twelve national expeditions wintered in Antarctica, intent on the scientific exploration of an area of the earth's surface nearly twice as large as Australia. The moving spirit in the meteorological programme was the late Harry Wexler, Chief of the U.S. Meteorological Service, who died suddenly in the spring of 1962 at the early age of 51. He left behind him a noble monument to his unique drive and professional skill in the clear picture we now have of the south polar vortex.

No one expected to find a replica of Rossby's polar vortex in the south. In the north, the conditions aloft are influenced by the enormous land masses of North America and northern Eurasia, and by the all but landlocked Arctic Ocean: as also by the unstable thermal equilibrium above the Caribbean. Antarctica, on the other hand, is bounded by the Southern Ocean: apart from the tip of South America, the nearest land mass – Australia – is upwards of 10,000 miles distant from the South Pole. The Antarctic Ocean current, unlike the ocean gyres we shall meet later in the ocean basins, encircles Antarctica as one fast-flowing west-east current in latitude 45° S.

And as the outcome of eight years of intensive study, centred on the United States 'Weather Central' by the Ross Sea, but carried out by a combined team of American, French, Russian and British Commonwealth citizens, there emerges a comparatively simple pattern of zonal circulation aloft, and of the 'ventilation' (to use Harry Wexler's evocative expression) of the south polar vortex by winds from the north.

The mid-winter circulation high aloft over Antarctica is one of strong westerly winds circling an area of low pressure over the pole, to be replaced in the Antarctic summer by a high when the warming of the upper atmosphere by the twenty-four-hour day sun is complete. There is none of the instability of the north-polar jet stream in the south, no sporadic cut-offs of masses of air south and north. The core of the Antarctic vortex, the south polar jet stream, is a true geostrophic wind all the year round.

During the Antarctic winter, strong cyclonic storms sweep the lower reaches of the high-lying Antarctic plateau, which,

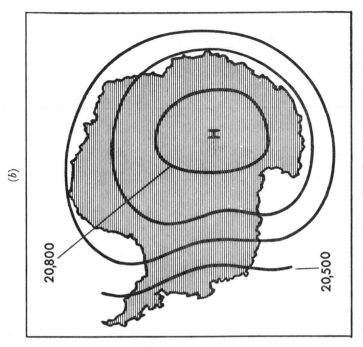

(b)

20,800

20,500

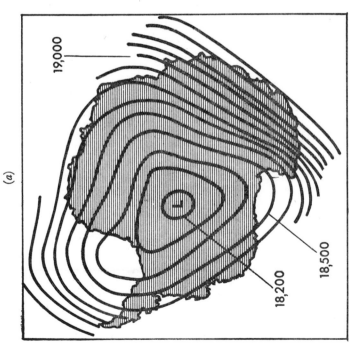

(a)

19,000

18,200

18,500

(4a). (5b). Circumpolar circulation, winter and summer, approximately 20,000 metres, or 65,000 feet, above the Antarctic continent.

however, never penetrate to the centre of the Antarctic continent. Since cyclones in the southern hemisphere spiral clockwise under the action of the Coriolis force (see Fig. 5.6), these storms sweep in the same sense about the pole as does the south polar vortex: consequently, violent turbulence in the upper reaches of the atmosphere is here absent.

The origin of these storms lies far to the north, around latitude 30°S, where gigantic sub-tropical cyclones (rotating clockwise) form over the warm ocean, to sail south before the westerlies of the southern hemisphere. These cyclones, warm and wet, transport heat and water vapour to Antarctica, which would otherwise be starved of both. Tiros IV, Wexler's 'weather eye', caught one of them making south on May 18 1962 (see Plate XXII).

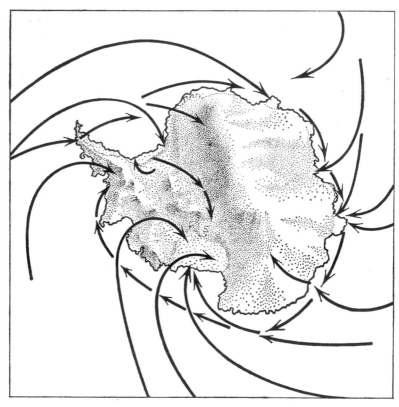

5.5. Winter storms in Antarctica.

126

The cold dry air over the Antarctic plateau is carried coastward by the so-called 'katabatic winds', which are such a marked feature of Antarctic weather. They flow downwards over the slopes which form the outer zone of the continental land mass at a speed of 20 knots or more. This shoreward flow is normally quite smooth; but it can become suddenly turbulent, and trigger the dreaded Antarctic blizzard, if the speed of flow exceeds a certain critical value appropriate to the local terrain.

Our sketch of the south polar vortex, and of the simple mechanism of its ventilation in the exchange of cold dry air for air that is warm and wet, is complete.

From Munster's Cosmographia (New York Public Library).

It all began with the trade-wind clouds, and ended with the gigantic clockwise cyclone above Antarctica. But at the risk of being accused of an act of regurgitation, one is obliged to emphasise once again that the planetary wind field is a fenced-in paddock, that the music of the four winds goes round and round and comes out nowhere at all, that the feed-back controlling any one-directional mechanism in the set-up of the earth's atmosphere is so strong that a description of its general circulation could legitimately start with an account of the local weather conditions over the British Isles or the Jamaicas. The Tiros satellites, coupled more than fortunately with the advent of high performance electronic computers, may well put a new complexion within our own lifetime on the whole complex mathematical and indeed didactic problem. But the time is not quite yet.

The time *has* come, however, to review once more in this book the planetary wind system: but now in a more succinct analytical form, rather than in the former descriptive fashion, in which he who ran might read.

Thus we enter on our résumé with the effect of a spinning earth on every particle of air or water in the atmosphere or the oceans. Now the trade winds, with which we began, are first launched from dry high pressure areas in the Horse Latitudes, around 30° north and south of the Equator, as winds that are flowing due south or due north as the case may be. Quite quickly, however, they become the 'easterlies' of the northern and southern hemispheres, under the combined effect of the so-called *Coriolis force* and of the *frictional drag* of their passage over the air/sea interface.

Everybody who has held vigil with the fixed stars in the eastern sky on a summer's night in northern latitudes has seen the horizon sweeping beneath them in a left-hand turn: an observer in the southern latitudes sees it as a right-hand turn. In other words, the earth is spinning anti-clockwise within the primary frame of reference of the fixed stars; and so if we aim to describe with mathematical precision the motion of an object moving over the earth's surface, or through the air above it or under the water of the oceans, we must refer that motion to a system of co-ordinate axes held steady in the framework of the stars.

This idealised procedure can however become very cumbersome when describing the complex motions of the winds and the ocean currents: and so we have recourse to a trick invented by Gaspard Gustave de Coriolis away back in 1835: we pretend

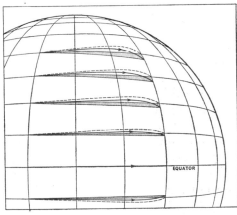

5.6. *The Coriolis force on a rocket projected horizontally towards the east, at four different latitudes in the northern hemisphere. The Coriolis force, acting to deflect the rocket to the right (or southward) of its direction of motion, decreases steadily with decreasing latitude to the value zero at the Equator.*

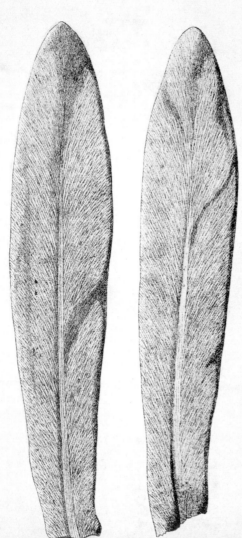

Above, two species
of Equisetales, or
'Horse tails', fossils
found in the
Allegheny
carboniferous
deposits in the
United States;
their botanical
names are
*Asterophyllites
equisetiformis* and
(appropriately
enough) *Annularia
asteris* respectively.
The picture in the
top right-hand
corner shows the
terminal leaves of a
branch of *A.
equisetiformis* still
unfolded.
Below are shown
two leaves of
Glossopteris decipiens
from the State of
Bihar in India. The
contrast between
these tongue-shaped
leaves of the
temperate zone
carboniferous forests
and the horse-tail
form of the tropical
giants is so marked
as to need no
further explanation.

Plate XVII

Plate XVIII

Two ends of the same Laurasian transcurrent fault—the Cabot Fault in Nova Scotia and the Great Glen of the Scottish Highlands.

The upper picture shows Sunrise Valley on the Cabot Trail, sheltered by the tree-covered slopes of the North Mountain; below is Loch Oich, with Loch Linnhe in the southern distance and Invergarry Castle in the foregound.

The San Andreas Fault, looking north from the air above Indio, California.

Plate XIX

Trade wind clouds voyaging south to the Equator.

Plate XX

Cloud-tower water-vapour pump in full action, caught by an airborne camera off Puerto Rico at a height of 5,000 feet.

The trade-wind cell. . . .
See how the surface
easterlies of the northern
and southern sub-tropics
converge at the Equator
and are swept aloft.
Edging north and south
in turbulent eddies 20,000
feet above the earth's
surface, the once moisture-
laden air, now dry and
cold, meets the sub-
tropical jet-streams –
geostrophic winds circling
the earth in latitudes 30°N
and 30°S respectively –
up under the roof of the
troposphere. Compressed
against the barrier of the
jet-streams, the cold dry
air sinks to earth, where it
diverges north and south,
south and north – to
give us our surface
westerlies north and south
of 30°N and 30°S, and a
rebirth of the surface
trades blowing towards
the Equator.

Plate XXI

Plate XXII

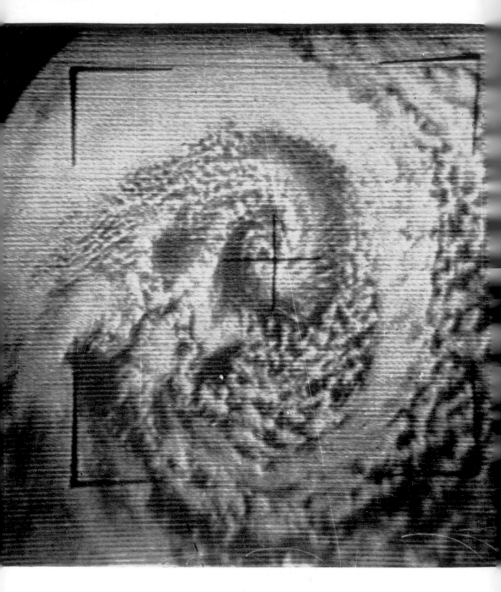

Cyclone photographed by TIROS IV, May 18 1962, in Lat. 8°E, Long. 50°S approx.

How the off-shore winds of the winter monsoon give rise to the up-welling of bottom water. The consequent increase in the photo-synthesised phytoplankton of the surface waters is dramatic. The life chain of the sea uncoils link by link. Soon the big edible fish converge on the nutrient area. Empty bellies ashore are filled.

Plate XXIII

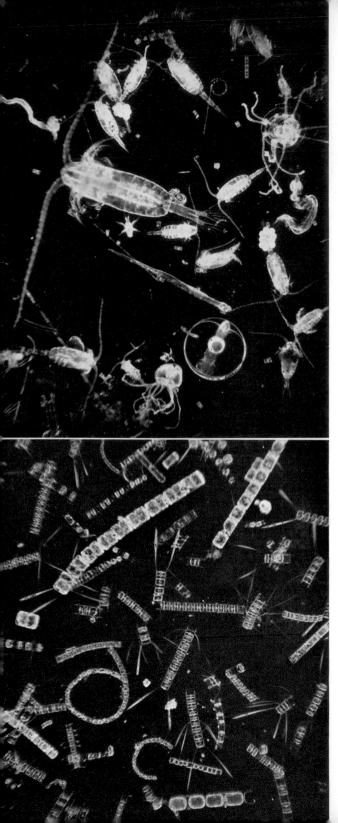

THE TEEMING LIFE OF THE SURFACE WATERS OF THE WORLD OCEAN.

Phytoplankton, the grass of the sea meadows. . . . At least three different families can be distinguished: several species of *Chaetoceros* (diatoms in chains armed with spines); *Thalassiosira condensata* (the shining white chain at bottom left); and *Lauderia borealis* to the right of the last named. (Magnification 120)

Zooplankton, first link in the chain of animal life in the sea. . . . Here we have two species of copepod (one represented by the largest animal present, the other by several specimens of a smaller variety, two with a cluster of eggs); two little medusas, with their circular domes and long tentacles; a circular fish egg at left centre, with a young arrow-worm to its right; a larval copepod between the arrow-worm and the large copepod; and two tunicate worms (top right and bottom centre). (Magnification 16)

Plate XXIV

that the earth is at rest, and ascribe the observed trajectories of objects moving within the fixed frame of reference of the stars to an imaginary force, the Coriolis force, urging a particle moving horizontally to the earth's surface to change its direction of motion to one *at right angles* to its direction at any instant: towards the *right* in northern latitudes, towards the *left* in southern latitudes.

Moreover, the *strength* of the Coriolis force is a maximum at the poles, dropping with decreasing latitude to zero at the Equator: a statement that can be visualised rather easily by imagining a rocket to be projected horizontally, first due east or west at the North Pole, then due east or west at the Equator. In the first case our hypothetical rocket would appear to be strongly deflected towards the right; at the Equator it would sail over the horizon strictly in the line of fire.

That is the qualitative description. Quantitatively it can be put in the form of a simple mathematical equation.

Thus

$$C = (2.\omega_e.\sin\varphi)u = f.u$$

where C is the Coriolis force per unit mass, ω_e is the angular velocity of rotation of the earth, φ is the latitude, and u is the eastward component of the velocity of a particle of air or water relative to the earth; while the quantity $2\omega_e\sin\varphi = f$ is known as the *Coriolis parameter*.

Note that the argument which has been developed above for an east-west motion over the earth's surface applies equally to a north-south motion. Thus if v is the velocity of a particle toward the north, the Coriolis force C acting on it is f.v.

Thus the *easterlies* of the trade winds, both north and south of the Equator, are neatly accounted for. They are winds that started out equatorwards, but which have been deflected *to the right* in the northern latitudes, *to the left* in the southern: winds moreover that have been restrained from swinging through a right angle to their initial direction, to become *east winds* rather than *easterlies*, by the friction set up at the air/sea interface.

Clearly, the easterlies of the Trades are moving partly against the west-to-east rotation of the earth. Therefore in their frictional passage over land, but chiefly over the sea, they borrow a fraction of the rotational momentum of the spinning

I

earth. This debt must be repaid, otherwise the whole general circulation of the atmosphere would grind to a stop.

This was first pointed out as late as 1926 by Harold Jeffreys of Cambridge, who in discovering the solution of the very difficult problem of *how* the stolen momentum is restored to its original possessor — the earth – builded better than he knew, as we shall see in a moment. Jeffreys began by considering not only the surface easterlies at the bottom of the trade-wind cycle, but also the surface westerlies (as distinct from the high-level polar vortices) which flow poleward north and south of the Horse Latitudes. These are winds which have a component moving *with* the rotation of the earth, and hence *part* with some of their own momentum in their passage poleward. Moreover, the frictional area of the earth's surface lying beneath the westerlies nicely balances that beneath the easterlies.

The problem is thus reduced to a single interrogation: What is the *mechanism* of the momentum exchange between the easterlies and the westerlies, required to restore the momentum balance over the whole system of earth and atmosphere, so that there is no net loss or gain to either? Jeffreys pointed out that this end can only be achieved by the turbulent mixing of air eddies high above ground across the boundary between the two systems.

Now comes the dramatic climax: for a mathematical analysis, more than somewhat abstruse, shows that such turbulent mixing is most readily achieved across a boundary for which the increase in wind velocity in a vertical direction is a maximum. And in the 1940's, not only were the required turbulent eddies aloft in the trade-wind cells actually observed by high-flying balloons and aircraft, but the sub-tropical jet streams were discovered, flowing under the roof of the atmosphere 30° north and south of the Equator, directly above the calms of the Horse Latitudes at sea level!

The conditions are very different in the polar vortices, for at 20,000 feet the frictional drag of the rotating earth is absent. The winds of the circumpolar whirls are essentially *geostrophic*, or 'earth-turned' winds, tracing out great circles over the globe high aloft – as indeed do the sub-tropical jet streams.

Geostrophic winds are born of two opposing forces: the Coriolis force, and the so-called *pressure gradient force*. Taking the north polar jet stream as a specific example – a wind blowing from west to east – we see at once that the Coriolis force is acting on it in a direction pointing due south. But as it whirls about the pole the particles of air in the stream are thrown southwards by centrifugal force, where they build up a higher pressure on the outer rim of the jet stream than on the inner rim, which is depleted of air particles by the same action of centrifugal force. In other words, a *pressure gradient* is established across the jet stream from south to north, such that the pressure gradient force directed due north exactly balances the Coriolis force directed due south. The jet stream during its quiescent periods is a true geostrophic wind.

In its periods of so-called 'meandering' (a weak word to describe the lashing of an aerial whip) the 4,000-mile-wide waves of the circumpolar vortex gave birth to families of *cyclones* along the eastern seaboard of North America, and calved isolated *anticyclones* over the sub-tropical seas. Let us take a closer look at these areas of low pressure and high pressure respectively – the 'lows' and 'highs' of the meteorologist.

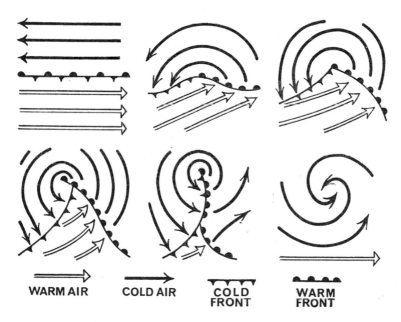

WARM AIR   COLD AIR   COLD FRONT   WARM FRONT

5.7. *The birth of a cyclone on the warm/cold 'front' off the east coast of North America.*

The life history of the cyclones of the northern hemisphere was first written down in the early twenties by the Bergen school of meteorologists in Norway, under the inspiration of Vilhelm and Jakob Bjerknes, father and son. Twenty years before their most outstanding pupil, Carl Gustav Rossby, had unravelled the aerodynamics of the polar vortex, they argued that the typical depression of the temperate latitudes must begin as a *wave* at the boundary of two air streams, a cold dense air stream flowing south-east from the arctic circle, a warm light air stream flowing north-west from the sub-tropics.

And here in Fig. 5.7 is the world-famous diagram that Jakob Bjerknes and his pupil Harald Solberg drew in 1921, to explain the birth of the Western Atlantic cyclones.

In the final stage of the formation of a depression, all distinction between the parent air masses is lost: the depression detaches itself from the 'polar front' between the two air streams as a cyclone, a mass of air rotating anti-clockwise under the action of the Coriolis force of the spinning earth, circumscribed by winds which spiral inwards to the centre of the depression. The centre is cold, from its origins, and wet from the condensed water vapour of the warm air from the Caribbean, 'occluded' in the earlier stages of its formation.

The anticyclones of the northern latitudes have come north from the Azores, masses of dry air from aloft, warmed by compression as they descend from the upper atmosphere to the

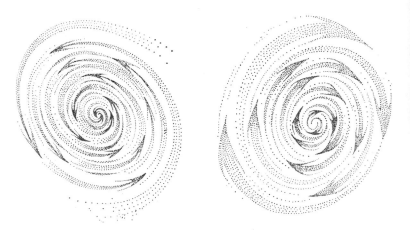

5.8. Cyclone and anti-cyclone in the northern hemisphere.

barometric 'high' at sea level. As such, they are areas of high pressure: anti-cyclonic winds flow outwards from the centre of the 'high', spiralling clockwise under the action of the Coriolis force.

In the southern hemisphere, of course, the direction of rotation of cyclones and anticyclones is reversed. Cyclones in southern latitudes spiral *clockwise*, since the Coriolis force on the inflowing winds acts to the *left* of their direction of motion, instead of to the *right*, as in the northern hemisphere. By the same token, anticyclones in southern latitudes spiral *anti-clockwise*.

In all the above, the word 'cyclone' should not be confused with the words 'hurricane' or 'typhoon'. These horrid winds with the girls' names have quite another and indeed seemingly capricious origin.

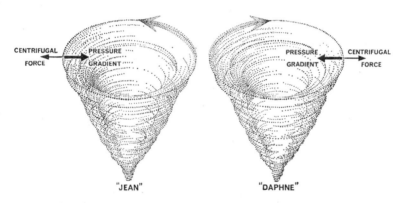

5.9. *Jean and Daphne, hurricane and typhoon, twisting counter-clockwise and clockwise respectively.*

In the jargon of the meteorologists, the flow of air in a hurricane or typhoon is described as 'cyclostrophic', in analogy with 'geostrophic'. In cyclostrophic motion the *centrifugal force*, acting outwards on the whirling mass of air, is balanced by the *pressure gradient force* acting inwards. As the air in the hurricane ascends, it becomes less dense: hence the radius of the typhoon increases, as you can see in Fig. 5.9.

Cyclostrophic rotation is so violent that it is freed entirely from the Coriolis force of the rotating earth, although the *initial* sense of rotation of a nascent typhoon may be given to it by the larger scale flow in which it is embedded: thus the hurricanes that harry the east coast of the United States rotate predominantly anticlockwise, the typhoons of the tropics predominantly clockwise, since their centres are alike areas of low pressure.

Hurricanes are born at the air/sea interface in tropical seas. That much can be written down with certainty. But the precise mechanics of 'cyclogenesis' is still a mystery. To quote from a recent publication on *Interaction between the Atmosphere and the Oceans* issued by the U.S. National Academy of Sciences in Washington:

"Most meteorologists agree that local heat sources over the oceans may be an essential element in the origin and maintenance of cyclonic disturbances over the oceans. For example, it is probable that hurricanes could not exist except for local heat sources. Another example may be found in the maintenance of vigorous nonfrontal cyclones over the subpolar oceans. The structure of these storms may be strongly modified by intense localized heat flow from the oceans during polar outbreaks. Still another probable example of air-sea interaction is the occurrence of preferred areas of cyclogenesis over the warm ocean currents off the east coasts of the continent.

"These cases serve to indicate the close ties that exist between comparatively local atmospheric and oceanic circulations – although in each instance the complete role of air-sea interaction is still unsolved. How and why do local anomalies in sea-surface temperature occur? Given an oceanic heat source, what are the mechanics and thermodynamics of the atmospheric reaction and the resulting 'feedback' to the ocean itself? After all, cyclonic development does not always occur, even in the case of isolated tropical vortices. Positive ocean temperature anomalies have been an attractive postulate for the origin of hurricanes for many years. Yet a satisfactory correlation has not been established, and climatically the location of highest frequency of hurricane formation does not coincide with the regions of warmest water."

Finally, let us review very briefly the concept of *vorticity*, so richly developed by Rossby, which we shall find quite indispensable in our later discussion of ocean currents.

Any volume of fluid at rest on the earth's surface anywhere but on the Equator is rotating in the fixed frame of reference of the stars, since there exists in all latitudes except zero latitude a local vertical component of the earth's rotation. Such a volume of fluid is said to possess 'planetary vorticity'. But there are many examples in meteorology and oceanography of a volume of air or water which has a tendency to spin around a vertical axis apart from that provided by the earth's rotation in space: such a volume of fluid possesses *relative vorticity* with respect to a fixed earth – and it is with such that we are chiefly concerned here.

Now relative vorticity can be changed either by a vertical stretching or shrinking of a column of the fluid (Fig. 5.10), or by a change of latitude (Fig. 5.11). Fig. 5.10 is self-explanatory; Fig. 5.11 needs some explanation. The barrel of viscous liquid which we may imagine with von Arx of Woods Hole to be carried from the North Pole by easy stages towards the Equator – very carefully, so as not to disturb its liquid contents – is at rest relative to the earth whenever we set it down. Not

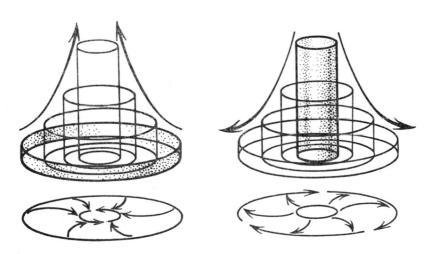

5.10. Shows how the relative vorticity of a column of fluid can be changed by vertical stretching or shrinking: giving rise to cyclonic motion of the fluid in the first case, anticyclonic motion in the second, under the action of the Coriolis force.

so the contents, which maintain the tendency to rotate anti-clockwise which they acquired from their container at the North Pole, *even when parked on the Equator.* On the other hand, if the barrel is carried north from the Equator, it will pick up the *planetary* vorticity appropriate to the local vertical, while the liquid contents remain at rest. But since anyone who took off the lid of the barrel to see how the contents were getting on would be rotating anti-clockwise around the local vertical along with the barrel, he would see the liquid rotating clockwise *relative to a fixed earth.*

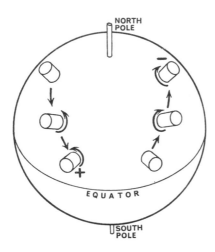

5.11. Illustrating the change of relative vorticity with latitude (after von Arx).

The vorticity theory has been applied with striking success by Walter Munk of La Jolla in California to the wind-driven circulation of the surface currents of the world's ocean basins.

One glance at a world map of the surface currents of the oceans instantly reveals a consistent picture of clockwise rotation in the northern hemisphere, of counter-clockwise rotation in the southern hemisphere, of a geostrophic circulation ringing Antarctica. But look more closely and there emerges a pattern of non-symmetrical circulation in the ocean basins: the currents are invariably narrower and stronger *on the western shores* of the oceans. We recognise the Gulf Stream in the North Atlantic, the Brazil Current in the South Atlantic, the Kuro Shiwo Current off the Islands of Japan in the North Pacific.

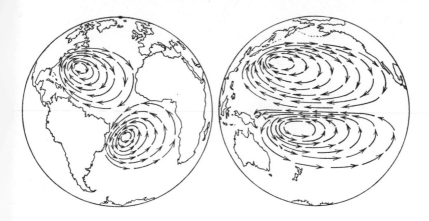

5.12. *The pattern of surface currents in the Atlantic and in the Pacific – ocean gyres rotating clockwise in the northern hemisphere, anti-clockwise in the south. The stark asymmetry of all four gyres springs to the eye, although they are the offspring of four tolerably symmetrical planetary windfields. Walter Munk of 'Scripps' has found an explanation of all this, which is set out fully in the text.*

Take the North Atlantic as a specific example. Here there is a gigantic anti-cyclonic or clockwise gyre of surface currents, generated at the air/ocean interface by the cat's-paws that streak before the easterly Trades of the tropics and the westerlies of the middle latitudes. This ocean gyre would be symmetrical about a central point in the Atlantic were it not that the vertical water columns moving north in the western quarter of the ocean and south in the eastern quarter acquire clockwise and anti-clockwise vorticity respectively in their passage north and south: always subject to the action of the Coriolis force, which increases in strength polewards, diminishes in strength equatorwards.

Thus the Coriolis force, acting to the right of the direction of motion in the North Atlantic, tends to *increase* the clockwise rotation of a column of water moving north along the eastern border of North America, and by the same token to *decrease* the rate of anti-clockwise rotation of a column moving south off the coast of Africa. Hence the influence of the Coriolis force alone would lead to an unlimited increase of the vorticity of the ocean gyre as a whole: and we must look for a feedback mechanism which will restrain such a runaway system and ensure a condition of stable equilibrium.

K   137

Munk finds the needed brake in friction between the boundaries of the ocean gyre and the edges of the adjacent land masses. On the eastern side, the diminishing strength of the Coriolis force as the boundary of the gyre moves equatorward allows a slow broad drift southwards, without appreciable friction at the coast-line. On the western side, however, the increase in the strength of the Coriolis force, here aided by the tendency toward vertical shrinkage of a water column transported northward into ever colder waters, acts to produce an always greater clockwise vorticity in a vertical water column as the current flows north, thus demanding a strong interaction with the coast. This leads to the production of a shearing force, opposing the current and inducing an anti-clockwise frictionally generated vorticity to balance that generated by the Coriolis force. Hence the strong narrow current of the Gulf Stream.

To sum up: a perfectly symmetrical planetary wind field, set up by the Trades and westerlies, has produced a strongly asymmetric ocean gyre in the surface waters of the North Atlantic, by a feed-back mechanism induced by that same rotation of the earth as gave rise to the Trades and westerlies. No wonder Deacon remarked that you might as well say that the Gulf Stream was as much responsible for the Trades as vice versa.

The next question is: How far below the surface does the *direct* influence of the atmosphere on the waters of the world ocean extend? The answer is always the same: a sharp vertical division of the ocean into an upper layer, of just over half a mile, wherein the water rapidly becomes both colder and less salty with depth; and a lower layer, in which temperature and salinity remain nearly constant all the way down to the ocean floor.

It is on this foundation that Henry Stommel, of Woods Hole Oceanographic Institute in New England, has developed his brilliant theory of the 'two-level ocean', which already carries the sign-manual of all good theories – it predicts the right results.

Stommel postulates a two-layer ocean, in which water from the upper layer sinks to the lower layer in the sub-arctic region, and rises from the lower to the upper layer in the sub-antarctic. He has not attempted so far to say why this should be so: in other words, his is essentially a 'phenomenological theory', in

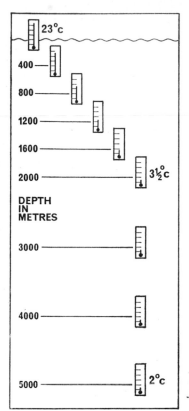

5.13. The so-called 'thermocline' – the top layer of the oceans in which the temperature falls steadily with increasing depth below surface.

5.14. Henry Stommel's idealised 'two-layer ocean'.

which careful analysis of a multitude of empirical data leads to an inspired guess – after which the argument is developed with strict attention to logic.

Pinpointing our attention now on the Atlantic, we should expect, on the two-layer theory, that the Antarctic bottom water rises to the upper layer in the South Atlantic, opposite the coast of Argentina: a result which is actually in good agreement with a full analysis of the results of the *Discovery II* cruises in the southern seas in the years 1929–30.

The map at Fig. 5.15 shows two major features: first that below the Gulf Stream must flow a deep-sea counter-current; second, that the Brazil Current has no such deep-sea counter-

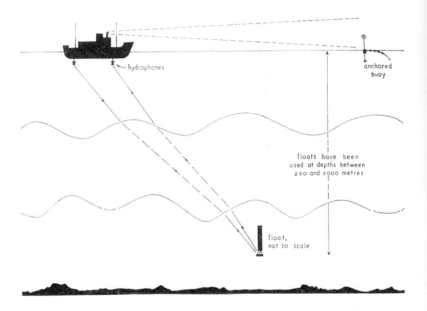

5.15. The 'Swallow Float', alias 'the Pinger'. . . . The float proper consists of a bundle of hollow compressible aluminium tubes, which can be loaded to make the float 'neutrally buoyant' at a pre-chosen depth in sea water: it is in fact a sort of air-balloon in reverse. The float is let down over the side of the mother ship on two long wires – long enough to allow it to drift with the undersea current at the predetermined depth. The wires are connected each to one of two hydrophones installed below the keel of the mother ship, which is now hove-to head to wind. Its position is found and followed by means of radar 'fixes' on an anchored buoy; that of the float by noting the difference in time of arrival of sonar pulses from the float's built-in transmitter at the two hydrophones, as the mother ship falls away from the wind direction. (Courtesy the British National Institute of Oceanography.)

current, and so to maintain equilibrium of the general circulation should be weaker than the Gulf Stream – which indeed it is.

In April 1957 the *Atlantis* from Woods Hole in New England and the *Discovery II* from the United Kingdom joined forces off the coast of Florida to search for Stommel's deep-sea counter-current to the Gulf Stream. The Americans contributed their most refined techniques for the measurement of temperature and salinity; the British brought along the Swallow float, to be immediately dubbed 'the pinger' by the American colleagues. Fig. 5.16 shows where they found the counter-current, of the predicted strength and at the predicted depth.

Now these theories and discoveries of modern oceanography about the run of the deep-sea currents are of no mere academic interest. They are of vital importance to mankind in at least two directions.

First, there is the problem of the disposal of industrial radioactive waste in the atomic age. It is of no use light-heartedly to jettison the countless tons of it which will accumulate from the nuclear reactors of the future on the ocean bottom in mid-Atlantic, in the pious hope that it will stay there. We have only to look at Stommel's map, and concentrate on the points of down-welling in the sub-arctic and up-welling in the sub-antarctic, to realise that. No: we must first learn much more about the deep circulation of the oceans before we can say that here and here and here are safe places for the dumping of atomic waste.

Second, there is the literally crying need to garner the living harvest of the sea, that we may fill the hungry stomachs of an already overpopulated world. There must be a change-over from hunting to husbandry in the catching of fish. Fish, as any oceanographer will tell you, are the best oceanographers in the world. They know the ocean currents backwards. So must we, or perish.

And in point of fact, a major international attack on a general oceanographic problem is even now under way: the International Indian Ocean Expedition 1963–65, a mass attack on the least-known ocean of the world by upwards of 50 ocean-going vessels flying a dozen different national flags.

No great enterprise such as this ever took shape of itself. There must first come the idea, springing to life in the mind of a

5.16. *The counter-current to the Gulf Stream, predicted by Stommel in 1956 and found by Discovery II and Atlantis in April 1957*

man. That man was Columbus O'Donnell Iselin, Director of the Woods Hole Oceanographic Institute in New England, who in the fall of 1957 proposed an 'Indian Ocean Year' as the first task of the newly formed Special Committee on Oceanic Research of the International Council of Scientific Unions (SCOR).

The scientific planning for what has become the International Indian Ocean Expedition was done by the working oceanographers of the world – American, Australian, British, Canadian, Danish, French, German, Indian, Japanese, Russian – in the three short years between 1957 and 1960; the strong national participation in the 'IIOE' is largely the work of the Coordinator for SCOR Planning, Robert G. Snider of New York, which he carried out between 1959 and 1962. In 1962 the logistics of the whole enterprise were taken over by UNESCO and the newly formed Intergovernmental Oceanographic Commission. They reap where others have sown.

The programme which the working scientists laid down in Copenhagen and Helsinki in the summer of 1960 is the most comprehensive programme to date in the young science of Oceanography. And here it is in brief summary:

One chief reason for the choice by SCOR of the Indian Ocean for a first exercise in international co-operative oceanic research was to make a test of Walter Munk's ideas about the action of the winds in creating surface currents. The wind system of the Indian Ocean basin is conditioned by the seasonal monsoons, which change direction as landward winds in summer to off-shore winds in winter – once every six months, in other words. Here then is a golden opportunity for research vessels which are prepared to brave the monsoon seasons to trace the detailed mechanism of the creation of surface currents by the prevailing winds, and to learn how far below surface, and at what rate, the influence of the winds extends; to answer the questions as to how rapidly the surface currents are formed by the winds, and the time lag of their reversal at the change-over of the monsoons.

Below surface, there is the possibility of elucidating the riddle of the equatorial current (and its counter-current already discovered both in the Pacific and later in the Atlantic) in relation to Stommel's two-layer theory of deep-water circulation: for the conditions prevailing in the Indian Ocean are so

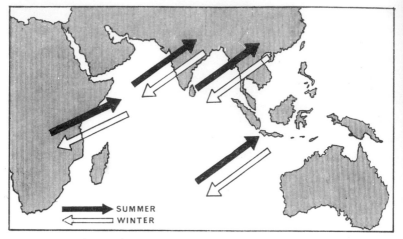

SUMMER
WINTER

5.17. The monsoons change direction each six months in the year.

different from those in the Atlantic and in the Pacific that a detailed knowledge of the equatorial circulation in the Indian Ocean could well shed new light on the finer details of deep-water circulation in all the oceans of the world.

Then again, the Indian Ocean is unique in the prevalence of strong off-shore winds for six months in the year. Such offshore winds pile up ocean water miles from the coast, leaving a hydro-static deficit in the water column coastwards (Plate XXIII). This leads to the *upwelling* of bottom water to fill the hydro-static 'vacuum', bringing nutrient salts to the surface which violently accelerate the rate of production of both plant and animal plankton in the surface waters, and a resultant enormous temporary increase in the population of edible fishes. Too, there are empty stomachs to fill in the lands bordering on the Indian Ocean, thankful for a plankton sandwich which in the not too far distant future may well be forthcoming, from a *controlled* upwelling induced by the installation on the sea bottom, at strategic points indicated by the IOE, of nuclear reactors whose primary product shall be life rather than death.

The bottom of the Indian Ocean has been but sketchily charted to date. Here the outstanding need is a detailed know-ledge of the run of the mid-ocean ridge and its all-important spinal rift valley. In the spring of 1962, as already noted, H.M.S. *Owen* brought back news of the expected existence of the rift in the Carlsberg Ridge: surely the first-fruits only of a rich harvest.

But there are many other geophysical-geological problems peculiar to the Indian Ocean: the curiously continental character of the islands of the Seychelles; the suspected existence of ocean-bottom trenches in the Andaman Sea; the accurate delineation of the local basins of the Indian Ocean, such as have already been extensively mapped in the Atlantic, which is so important for a knowledge of the distribution of fish species; the reconstruction of ancient climates from a study of cores brought up from the ocean-bottom sediments.

And the meteorologists are hungrily seizing a unique opportunity for the synoptic study of the interchange of water vapour, heat, and momentum across the air/ocean interface; of the exchange of gases – oxygen, nitrogen, carbon dioxide – between atmosphere and oceans; of the balance over an extended region of the earth's surface between evaporation of water vapour from the oceans, and its precipitation following condensation upon salt nuclei caught up into the atmosphere from sea spray.

The exchange of gases is a topic barely touched on so far in this chapter. This is not because it is unimportant to a complete understanding of the mode of action of the atmosphere/ocean heat engine – on the contrary – but because so little is yet known about it. Apart from a parcel of weather ships in the North Atlantic, there are scarcely any stationary observation posts – even islands – so necessary for standardised synoptic observation of meteorlorogical processes occurring at the same time at different places. That is why meteorologists have greeted the opportunity offered by the Indian Ocean Expedition so eagerly: opportunities accruing from the close geographical network proposed by Bob Snider, at the points of intersection of which research vessels will lay-to for comparatively long periods, for the purpose of collecting core samples from the bottom sediments and of taking pictures of the ocean floor.

To quote once again from the U.S. National Academy's hand-out *Interaction between the Atmosphere and the Oceans*:

"The *oxygen distribution* in the sea is of the utmost importance in marine biology and to some extent in physical and general oceanography. One source of oxygen is the atmosphere; another is photo-synthesis in the upper water levels. There is evidence that oxygen passes in both directions through the sea surface, perhaps sometimes influenced by the season of the year. However, the factors which control the rate of transmission of oxygen through the air-sea interface are poorly understood."

Again, a better knowledge of the exchange of CO_2 between atmosphere and ocean is greatly to be desired. Carbon dioxide, as we have seen, is one of the constituents of the earth's 'greenhouse without glass', which sets the climatic thermometer at its present temperate average level. But mankind in the industrial age has been spewing CO_2 into the atmosphere, from factory chimneys, chemical works and car exhausts, at a rate of some 10 billion tons per annum as against a total atmospheric content of rather less than 3 trillion tons.

Now this is already an annual injection sufficient to affect quite seriously the radiation balance of the earth, unless there is some compensatory factor acting to restore the balance. To quote still again from *NAS Publication 983*:

"The accumulation of carbon dioxide in the atmosphere, resulting from our expanding industrial operations and other sources of combustion, is causing concern because of its possible eventual effect upon climate. Research is under way to determine the extent to which the ocean may control this by absorbing carbon dioxide. Thus far, it appears that such absorption may be slower and more ineffective than has heretofore been assumed. We need much more information on this point, however. There are certainly large regions on earth where the carbon dioxide tension in the water is greater than that in the atmosphere, and other regions where the reverse is true. We may assume, therefore, that carbon dioxide is passing both into and out of the water. The nature of this balance – its geographic and temporal variation – has not been established."

The exchange of *solids* between the atmosphere and the oceans has been a much neglected subject, and it is now realised that our understanding even of the overall balance between the evaporation of water from the ocean surface, and its return as rain condensed around dust particles and particles of sodium chloride – the salt of the sea – is quite inadequate: aside altogether from regional and local variations from the norm.

A final quotation from *NAS 983*:

"Further observations are required. The vertical distribution of salt nuclei in the turbulent boundary layer of the atmosphere over the oceans; the rate at which such particles escape from the boundary layer to the free atmosphere, or return to the ocean surface; and the variations of these factors as a function of the size of salt particles – all of these problems are virtually untouched. The mechanics of spray formation, which apparently plays a fundamental role in the process whereby salt particles find their way into the atmosphere, needs additional study. There is evidence that condensation nuclei are supplied to the atmosphere at highly variable rates, depending strongly upon the state of the sea and the wind speed. Localised intense production of salt particles may be related in some unknown way to the distribution of precipitation over the ocean."

One last subject, and a sore one at that. A small but significant fraction of the CO_2 absorbed by the oceans is radio-active, containing as it does the radio-active isotope of ordinary 'carbon-twelve', namely 'carbon-fourteen' formed from the nitrogen in the atmosphere under the natural bombardment of cosmic rays. Now just as $C14$ has proved an invaluable tool in the modern dating of archaeological finds, so it could be used to determine the comparative ages of different areas of deep-sea water, and hence the run of the deep-sea currents – were it not for the fact that the earth's atmosphere has been contaminated ever since 1945 by radio-active carbon spawned by A-bomb and H-bomb tests over Bikini, Christmas Island and Nova Zembla. The oceans have likewise been contaminated, so that no one knows the natural $C14$ content of seawater prior to the advent of the atomic age and the discovery of the $C14$ method of age determination.

And man's contamination of his own environment doesn't

end with the testing of atomic war-heads. In one single year we have witnessed an attempt – a fumbled one at that – in the fall of 1961, to put a band of copper needles round the earth, at the risk of ruining the science of Radio-astronomy; and still more unforgivable, the so-called 'Rainbow Bomb', exploded with breath-taking irresponsibility 500 miles above earth on July 9 1962, which filled the Van Allen belts – the proudest discovery of the IGY – for years to come with a man-made broth of unnatural electrons.

Scientists who have lent themselves to special pleading before such events have at worst been guilty of a sin against their profession, and at least have lost face opposite a public opinion which was already getting more than a little tired of their pompous *ex cathedra* pronouncements in the press and from the goggle-box. Such men have sold their scientific birthright for a mess of gift-coupon pottage.

If there is one single lesson to be learned from a study of the earth it is this: that man is a part of his environment, that he is at once actor and spectator in the drama of life; that he lives within a system subject to the fiercest feed-back controls, that will surely recoil upon him if he thoughtlessly meddles with them. Let us hope (against the hope that long deferred leaves a thinking mind sick) that his exploration of the planets in the Space Age – worlds which were born along with his own 5,000 million years ago from our parent sun – will be made with clean hands, pure heart, and humble voice.

INDEX